An individual having unusual difficulties in coping with his environment struggles and kicks up the dust, as it were. I have used the figure of a fish caught on a hook: his gyrations must look peculiar to other fish that don't understand the circumstances; but his splashes are not his affliction, they are his effort to get rid of his affliction and as every fisherman knows these efforts may succeed.

Karl Menninger

This publication has been produced by the British Psychological Society Division of Clinical Psychology and represents the views and expert contributions of the members of that Division only.

For all enquiries please email membernetworkservices@bps.org.uk (putting 'Understanding Psychosis' in the subject line)
or telephone 0116 252 9515.

ISBN: 978-1-85433-748-1

Revised version 2017, originally published 2014.

© British Psychological Society 2017

Editor: Anne Cooke

Art by: Anita Klein (www.anitaklein.com)
Many thanks to Anita for kindly allowing us to use her beautiful paintings free of charge.

Contributors:*

Thurstine Basset
Professor Richard Bentall
Professor Mary Boyle
Anne Cooke (co-ordinating editor)
Caroline Cupitt
Jacqui Dillon
Professor Daniel Freeman
Professor Philippa Garety
Dr David Harper
Dr Lucy Johnstone
Professor Peter Kinderman
Professor Elizabeth Kuipers
Professor Tony Lavender

Laura Lea
Dr Eleanor Longden
Dr Rufus May
Professor Tony Morrison
Dr Sara Meddings
Professor Steve Onyett
Dr Emmanuelle Peters
Professor David Pilgrim
Professor John Read
Professor Mike Slade
Yan Weaver
Professor Dame Til Wykes

Acknowledgements
We are very grateful to
- Canterbury Christ Church University for supporting Anne Cooke to undertake this project;
- Dr Catherine Dooley, Dr Stephen Weatherhead and the Professional Standards Unit of the Division for commissioning and supporting this report;
- Dr Stuart Whomsley and the Psychosis and Complex Mental Health Faculty of the Division for helpful comments and support;
- Sophie Chatfield and Sarah Phillips for their skilled and enthusiastic help with research and referencing;
- Bruce Bassam for help and support over the course of this project;
- Helen and Nigel Cooke for helpful comments on making our language clear and accessible;
- Professor Peter Kinderman for his extensive help and support with the editing process;
- Dr Jayasree Kalathil and colleagues. Following the launch of this report, the editor Anne Cooke received an open letter signed by Dr Kalathil, Professor Suman Fernando, Professor Philip Thomas and Dr Jan Wallcraft. It pointed out that the report had engaged insufficiently with scholarship regarding the experiences of people from black and minority ethnic communities in relation to psychosis and schizophrenia,[1] that people from these communities were not represented on the author group, and that changes were needed to the language in some sections. Anne apologised for this and a number of meetings took place to address these issues. This revised version published in 2017 includes amendments addressing these issues and also the relationship between psychosis and social inequality more generally, drafted in consultation with the signatories and with Professor Nimisha Patel. Other critiques of the report will be addressed in future editions. This revised version of the original edition is dedicated to contributor Steve Onyett who sadly passed away in 2015. His contribution to improving mental health care was immense. We miss you Steve;
- Dr David Harper and Professor David Pilgrim for their extensive contributions to the preparation of this revised version.

Contributors to the first report*
This report draws on and updates an earlier one, *Recent Advances in Understanding Mental Illness and Psychotic Experiences*, which was published in 2000.

Professor Richard Bentall
Professor Mary Boyle
Professor Paul Chadwick
Anne Cooke (co-ordinating editor)
Professor Philippa Garety
Dr Simon Gelsthorpe
Dr Anne Goodwin
Dr David Harper
Dr Lucy Johnstone

Professor Peter Kinderman (co-ordinating editor)
Professor Tony Lavender
Dr Rufus May
Professor Elizabeth Kuipers
Dr Steve Onyett
Dr Emmanuelle Peters
Professor David Pilgrim
Professor Mike Slade
Professor Dame Til Wykes

* Listed in alphabetical order. Contributor details are given at the end of the report.

Contents

Part 2: Causes: why do so many people have these experiences and when do they become distressing?

Part 3: What can help

Part 4: What we need to do differently

Foreword

This report provides an overview of the current state of knowledge about why some people hear voices, experience paranoia or have other experiences seen as 'psychosis'. It also describes what can help. In clinical language, the report concerns the 'causes and treatment of schizophrenia and other psychoses'. A parallel report is available entitled *Understanding Bipolar Disorder – Why People Experience Extreme Mood States, and What Can Help*[1]. In recent years we have made huge progress in understanding the psychology of what had previously often been thought of as a largely biological problem, an illness. Much has been written about the biological aspects: this report aims to redress the balance by concentrating on the psychological and social aspects, both in terms of how we understand these experiences and also what can help when they become distressing.

We hope that this report will contribute to a fundamental change that is already underway in how we as a society think about and offer help for 'psychosis' and 'schizophrenia'. For example, we hope that in future services will no longer insist that service users accept one particular view of their problem, namely the traditional view that they have an illness which needs to be treated primarily by medication. The report is intended as a resource for people who work in mental health services, people who use them and their friends and relatives, to help ensure that their conversations are as well informed and as useful as possible. It also contains vital information for those responsible for commissioning and designing both services and professional training, as well as for journalists and policy-makers. We hope that it will help to change the way that we as a society think about not only psychosis but also the other kinds of distress that are sometimes called mental illness.

Contributors

This report was written by a working party mainly comprised of clinical psychologists drawn from the NHS and universities, and brought together by their professional body, the British Psychological Society Division of Clinical Psychology. This report draws on and updates an earlier one, *Recent Advances in Understanding Mental Illness and Psychotic Experiences*, which was published in 2000 and was widely read and cited. The contributors are leading experts and researchers in the field; a full listing with affiliations is given at the end of the report. More than a quarter of the contributors are experts by experience – people who have themselves heard voices, experienced paranoia or received diagnoses such as psychosis or schizophrenia. At the end of the report there is an extensive list of websites, books and other resources that readers might find useful, together with list of the academic research and other literature that the report draws on.

Executive Summary

- This report describes a psychological approach to experiences that are commonly thought of as psychosis, or sometimes schizophrenia. It complements parallel reports on the experiences commonly thought of as bipolar disorder and depression.

- Hearing voices or feeling paranoid are common experiences which can often be a reaction to trauma, abuse or deprivation. Calling them symptoms of mental illness, psychosis or schizophrenia is only one way of thinking about them, with advantages and disadvantages.

- There is no clear dividing line between 'psychosis' and other thoughts, feelings and beliefs: psychosis can be understood and treated in the same way as other psychological problems such as anxiety or shyness. Significant progress has been made over the last twenty years both in understanding the psychology of these experiences and in finding ways to help.

- Some people find it useful to think of themselves as having an illness. Others prefer to think of their problems as, for example, an aspect of their personality which sometimes gets them into trouble but which they would not want to be without.

- In some cultures, experiences such as hearing voices are highly valued.

- Each individual's experiences are unique – no one person's problems, or ways of coping with them, are exactly the same as anyone else's.

- For many people, though not all, experiences such as hearing voices or feeling paranoid are short-lived. Even people who continue to experience them nevertheless often lead happy and successful lives.

- It is a myth that people who have these experiences are likely to be violent.

- Psychological therapies – talking treatments – are very helpful for many people. The National Institute for Health and Care Excellence recommends that everyone with a diagnosis of psychosis or schizophrenia should be offered talking therapy. However, currently most people are unable to access it.

- More generally, it is vital that services offer people the chance to talk in detail about their experiences and to make sense of what has happened to them. Surprisingly few currently do. Professionals should not insist that people accept any one particular framework of understanding, for example that their experiences are symptoms of an illness.

- Many people find that 'antipsychotic' medication helps to make the experiences less frequent, intense or distressing. However, there is no evidence that it corrects an underlying biological abnormality. Recent evidence also suggests that it carries significant risks, particularly if taken long term.

- Psychosis is often related to experiences of abuse, deprivation, victimisation and racism.

- There is also racism and other forms of discrimination in services. People from black and minority ethnic backgrounds, particularly young men, are more likely than others to be diagnosed with schizophrenia, more likely to experience compulsion, more likely to be given powerful drugs and less likely to be offered psychological therapy. In general people from disadvantaged backgrounds also get a worse deal from services.

- Services need to change radically, and we need to invest in prevention by taking measures to reduce abuse, deprivation and inequality.

Note on Terminology

There is considerable debate about the most helpful way of referring to the experiences described in this report. The different terms used by different people reflect the more general debate – which this report describes – about the nature and causes of these experiences.

Traditionally, experiences such as having extremely suspicious thoughts (paranoia) or hearing voices that no-one else can hear, have been seen as signs of mental illness, for example schizophrenia or bipolar disorder. People who experience them have been referred to as 'patients' or 'sufferers'. Whilst some people find this a helpful way of understanding what is going on, others do not, and many people do not see themselves as having an illness. Indeed, over the past twenty years it has become clear that there are many people in the general population who have these experiences but never need any kind of mental health care.

Throughout this report we have attempted to use terms which are as neutral as possible, and which do not imply that there is only one correct way of understanding these experiences. Consequently we refer to the experiences in question as 'experiences' rather than as 'symptoms'. We use the ordinary English terms such as hearing voices or feeling suspicious or paranoid. Sometimes we use the term 'psychosis' because it is the term in common use within our society to describe these experiences. We recognise that not everyone is comfortable with this term. In recognition that not everyone agrees that there is an underlying illness, we use the wording 'people diagnosed with' (schizophrenia, for example), rather than 'people with schizophrenia'. For the same reason we refer to people as people, rather than as patients.

Of course, much of what has been written previously in this area has used a clinical framework and has therefore used clinical or medical terminology. When describing this work we have sometimes used quotation marks round these terms.

Part 1: What is 'psychosis'?

Section 1: What this report is about: experiences sometimes called psychosis

Key points

This report presents a psychological perspective on the experiences that are commonly thought of as psychosis, or sometimes schizophrenia. It complements parallel reports on the experiences commonly thought of as bipolar disorder[1] and depression.[2]

These experiences include hearing voices ('hallucinations'), believing things that others find strange ('delusions'), speaking in a way that others find hard to follow ('thought disorder') and experiencing periods of confusion where you appear out of touch with reality ('acute psychosis').

Each individual's experiences are unique – no one person's experiences, or ways of coping with them, are exactly the same as anyone else's.

Many people who have these kinds of experiences do not come into contact with mental health services because they do not find their experiences distressing. Some people, however, are so distressed by them that they seek professional help, or others seek help on their behalf.

1.1 What does it mean to experience psychosis?

This report is about those experiences that are usually thought of as 'psychosis', 'schizophrenia', 'mental illness', 'nervous breakdown' or sometimes 'madness'. A tendency to experience extreme moods has also sometimes been seen as mental illness, in this case 'bipolar disorder'. Whilst many of the issues are similar, 'bipolar disorder' is the subject of a separate report[3] and so will not be discussed at length here.

The types of experience discussed in this report include:

* Hearing voices speaking when there is no-one there, or seeing, tasting, smelling or feeling things that other people do not. Sometimes these experiences have been called hallucinations.

* Holding strong beliefs that others around you do not share. An example would be a belief that there is a conspiracy against you by the CIA, or that someone else is controlling your thoughts. Sometimes these beliefs have been referred to as delusions. If they are about other people wanting to harm you, they have sometimes been called paranoid delusions. If they are about being special, they have sometimes been called grandiose delusions.

* Difficulties with thinking and concentrating. Whilst many people who have experiences such as those described here find ways to cope with them, or even find them helpful, for others they can at times be overwhelming. At such times it is often hard to concentrate on other things at the same time. People can appear distracted and preoccupied. They may talk back to voices that they are hearing. Sometimes people talk in a way that other people find hard to

follow, mentioning many apparently unrelated topics in quick succession. This has sometimes been referred to as 'thought disorder'. Many of us become somewhat 'thought disordered' and say confused or confusing things when we are emotionally stressed.[4]

- At times, some people may appear inexpressive, withdrawn, listless, apathetic or unmotivated. They may find it difficult even to find the energy to prepare food or generally to look after themselves. Traditionally these difficulties have been thought of as 'negative symptoms': part of an illness. However, they can often be a result of feeling overwhelmed by experiences and trying to cope, or arise from feelings of helplessness and depression. They can also be unwanted effects of the drugs that people are often prescribed.

Often these experiences occur at times of particular stress and are linked to strong emotions and feelings, for example worry, anxiety, fear, depression or feeling overwhelmed by events. Indeed there is no way of clearly separating 'psychotic' experiences from other emotional problems which might attract diagnoses such as anxiety or depression, or from problems resulting from trauma which might attract diagnoses such as 'post-traumatic stress' or 'personality disorder'.

Different experiences of psychosis

It's like the whole of the top of your head comes off. There's just this incredible rush of energy and, and hysteria almost. And, then I started to hallucinate visually, and I just saw this lovely garden, and I thought oh this is heaven. And by that point I was completely lost because then I had an alternative to that, and I really believed I was going to hell. I thought I was dying... I'm not desperately religious. And I woke up and Mum came into the room and I was completely gone. And we were kind of left to deal with it for a couple of days. I didn't understand what had happened to me. I really thought I was dying. So I picked up a Bible [laughter in voice] and read 'Revelations' which is not a very good thing to do. And for two minutes I actually believed that I was Christ, until I was logical enough to think, well I'm not male, so what's happening?

Rachel [5]

I began to think that... my blood had been poisoned by evil spirits and that I was evil, and that there were spirits around me, warping my thoughts and changing my thoughts, and that was very frightening and I didn't know what to do with it.

Graham [6]

Because I taught African and Caribbean culture, the transatlantic slave trade was a big part of my remit and I went into it a little bit too deeply. And then all of sudden something unlocked in me. I started hearing my ancestors. I could hear them crying and I could feel their pain. All my female ancestors, I could feel them and I could feel all their children. I could hear them on their voyage and I could feel all these people coming to me through all my reading. It started to affect me and that was a problem.

Anon [7]

Different experiences of psychosis

In 1986, at the age of 18, over a seven-month period I was admitted three times to psychiatric hospital. Initially I had experienced sleep deprivation and was very confused, holding some grandiose and paranoid beliefs. I believed the television and radio had interactive messages for me. I also believed I had unknowingly been a spy and that the world was like a combination of the books *1984*, and *Blade Runner*. Nothing was as it appeared, with robotic surveillance pets and sinister tracking devices.

I also saw familiar faces in strangers' faces, which lead to further espionage theories. I believed that I was in danger of losing my ability to think freely and spontaneously, that I would become an automaton as I reached full adulthood. My concentration was extremely poor. I was in a high state of vigilance, fear and tension, leading to psychosomatic chest pains. I also entertained other more spiritual beliefs focussing on good and evil and having special powers of communication. Due to having a family history of psychosis, it was easier for clinicians to quickly make a diagnosis of schizophrenia. My parents were told I had schizophrenia and that I would need to take medication for the rest of my life.

Rufus May, contributor [8]

I was diagnosed with a mental illness five years ago. I'm on tablets to suppress paranoia and voices. These work, except that sometimes I still experience paranoia. It's the worst feeling I've ever felt, and it comes on during the middle of the day and lasts till I go to sleep at night. I become paranoid about everything – that my keys are going to drop out of my bag, that my trousers are going to fall down, that the authorities will want to test me to see if I am really ill. I fear exposing myself in front of others, or saying something rude. I get mental pictures of me doing nasty things or them doing nasty things to me and yet something else is happening in reality... I would do anything to stop these feelings as all I want to do is run from everyone when I have them.

Miriam [9]

I was constantly being bombarded by terrifying voices. I believed they were all powerful entities that were always right. One of the voices I heard claimed he was the devil, another threw lewd insults at me such as 'whore' and told me he could kill anyone he wanted if I didn't do what he said, another controlled what I ate and berated me with insults about my appearance.

I fitted the voices I heard into my elaborate theories on life that to everyone around me, sounded like nothing more than the mad babblings of insanity. Theories of parallel universes, evil spirits, government conspiracies and special communications with the underworld and Satan himself.

I was regularly being sectioned by the local police force for attempting to jump from motorway bridges and in front of oncoming intercity trains. I often felt I needed to tell the world how doomed they all were, or announce I was 'onto them' and that usually ended in the back of a police car or ambulance on my way to A&E to be assessed by the mental health team.

Sally Edwards

Division of Clinical Psychology

1.2 Everyone's experiences are different

As with all human experiences, no one person's problems, or ways of coping with them, are exactly the same as anyone else's. Some people have only one of these experiences, others have several. Some people experience them on only one occasion, others from time to time (for example during periods of stress), and others frequently.[10]

Many people do not come into contact with mental health services because they do not find their experiences distressing.[11] For example, many people hear voices talking to them when there is no-one there, but the voices say relatively neutral, pleasant or even helpful things so this is not a problem. Others develop ways of coping with their experiences on their own or with help from people around them.[12] Some people, however, are so distressed by their experiences that they seek professional help. Some come to the attention of professionals because other people consider their behaviour odd or worrying, or fear that it is putting the person or others at risk. Only these last two groups of people are likely to come into contact with mental health services and to be diagnosed as mentally ill.

Helpful voices

I see the voices I hear as parts of myself that hold the strong emotions it didn't feel safe enough to feel. They are parts of me without which I would not have survived. To see them as a symptom of a mental illness is insulting, and failing to acknowledge their pivotal role in my survival as a human being. I want to thank them, not get rid of them!

Now, the voices are great friends and advisors. I would never want to get rid of them. I no longer identify with my previous role as a severely mentally ill psychiatric patient but a human being that is experiencing and surviving life in my own unique way... just like every other human being on this planet.

Sally Edwards

I have learnt over the years that the one voice that I used to hear in my head, which was just a general voice, was actually one of my main, I call them inspirers rather than guides... they help you.

Mary [13]

Are my experiences psychosis? Are they hallucinatory? Are they delusional and/or grandiose? What do your life, your learning and your culture provide by way of an answer? Within our Maori culture these experiences are nothing new. Generations have been born seeing, feeling, hearing and knowing... These things are not anomalous for the Maori. The anomaly happens when non-Maori perspective is applied to it... The end result from that perspective can only be that it is perceived as abnormal.

Egan Bidois [14]

1.3 Our different cultures

Our cultural background has a significant influence on what we experience, on how we interpret those experiences and on the forms of help we are likely to find most useful. In the UK, European beliefs and customs have been, and often still are implicitly assumed to be the norm. Some critics argue that Western psychiatry and psychology have in the past sometimes viewed whole groups of people as 'pathological' and acted as a form of 'cultural imperialism'.[15] For example, the South African psychologist Hendrik Verwoerd drew on eugenic theories to justify the racist policy of apartheid when he was Prime Minister in the 1950s and 1960s[16]. When one cultural group's customs are implicitly assumed to be the norm, this can create an 'us and them' situation, where cultural differences are misinterpreted and seen as problems or as 'abnormal'. This can apply to subcultures too: for example, many white British people belong to religious or other groups which believe in the ability to communicate with the dead or with aliens. It is important for professionals to maintain an attitude of respectful interest regarding the influence of culture on someone's mental health problems and to avoid making assumptions. Culture might affect the nature of a person's experience (e.g. what kind of voices they hear), the meaning they make of it, or how they describe and explain it. Sometimes, explanations used by people from minority ethnic backgrounds or from particular subcultures (for example particular religious groups) might seem strange to people from majority cultures. This can sometimes lead to misinterpretation and unhelpful responses from services. For example, someone from a particular religious group which believes in the possibility of demon possession might believe that he or she is possessed.

In trying to help someone, we need to take into account not only their distress but also their cultural background and circumstances. Often this can be complex: for example, in our multi-cultural society many people identify with aspects of more than one culture. Racism is also a problem that those of us from black and minority ethnic backgrounds often face and, as a result, many develop a degree of suspicion and wariness which is often a necessary survival mechanism. Some commentators refer to such wariness as 'healthy cultural paranoia'[17,18] but it may be misinterpreted by professionals as a symptom of psychosis unless they take the person's social context into account. Of course, racism may also in itself lead to mental health problems[19] (see section 6.1).

Section 2: How common are these experiences?

Key points

These experiences are common: up to 10 per cent of the general population hear voices at some point in their life, and very many people have beliefs that those around them find strange.

Whilst these experiences are very distressing for some, others have similar experiences but don't come into contact with mental health services because they don't find them particularly distressing.

Some people see them as helpful or even as spiritual experiences.

As we explain below, the idea that these experiences are symptoms of mental illnesses is a controversial one. Nevertheless, until recently much research published in academic journals was based on this assumption, and so the only estimates available tend to be numbers of people who have received a certain diagnosis. The past decade, however (since, indeed, the publication of our first report),[1] has seen a steady increase in research exploring individual experiences such as hearing voices.[2] Researchers have also discovered that many people will not be counted in any figures because they do not find their experiences distressing and therefore do not seek help from mental health professionals.[3] However, much research still relies on psychiatric diagnoses given to people who come into contact with services. Common diagnoses given to people who have these sorts of experiences are schizophrenia and bipolar disorder. Other terms that people might have encountered are: paranoia, psychosis, psychotic illness, delusional disorder, schizoaffective disorder, manic depression and psychotic depression.

2.1. How many people have 'psychotic' experiences? How many are given a diagnosis of schizophrenia?

These experiences are quite common. Up to 10 per cent of people will at some point in their life hear a voice talking to them when there is no-one there.[4] About one person in every hundred receives a diagnosis of schizophrenia, so there are probably about 500,000 people in the UK who have received the diagnosis. A similar number of people receive a diagnosis of bipolar disorder (also known as manic depression).[5] As we will make clear later in this report, there is a very great deal of variability in these figures – people's life circumstances affect both how likely they are to experience certain problems, and also how likely they then are to receive a certain diagnosis.

2.2. People who do not use mental health services

A number of surveys have revealed that many people hear voices regularly. Most of these people have never thought of themselves, or been thought of as mentally ill.[6] The main thing that appears to distinguish them from those who come into contact with mental health services is the extent to which they, or those around them, find the experience distressing or frightening. For example, someone might go to a doctor if they or their family members are worried that their beliefs or experiences might lead them to do something risky.[7] Similarly, a large proportion of the general population holds beliefs that others might consider unusual or paranoid, for example beliefs about alien abduction, ghosts or telepathy.[8] As we explain later, people's experiences vary in nature, frequency and intensity, and appear to lie on a continuum. In other words, many of us occasionally have puzzling experiences or hold some beliefs that others regard as peculiar or eccentric. Relatively fewer of us have frequent or severe experiences, or beliefs that others find strange and worrying.

People who have psychotic experiences but don't come into contact with services

When you can't find a way out when you get into a complex situation, they (voices) help guide you. You don't have to listen, you don't have to take their advice but it's nice that they give it anyway.

Karen [9]

Many people who have these experiences feel that they are very significant in their lives. Some people believe that they have religious or spiritual significance. Some explain them in terms of supernatural or religious forces, or see them as giving them a deeper understanding of, or insight into the world.[10]

Psychotic experiences and spiritual experiences

There are people who have developed a very positive relationship with the experience of hearing voices, and have managed without any psychiatric treatment or support. They have adopted a theoretical frame of reference (such as parapsychology, reincarnation, metaphysics, the collective unconscious, or the spirituality of a higher consciousness) which connects them with others rather than isolating them: they have found a perspective that offers them a language in which to share their experiences. They enjoy a feeling of acceptance; their own rights are recognised, and they develop a sense of identity which can help them to make constructive use of their experiences for the benefit of themselves and others.

Marius Romme & Sandra Escher [11]

Section 3: Are these experiences best understood as mental illness?

Key points

There is a debate about whether it is accurate and/or useful to think of experiences like hearing voices as symptoms of mental illness. A psychological approach aims to understand these experiences in the same way that we understand other thoughts and feelings.

As with other psychological problems, it makes sense to think of experiences like hearing voices in terms of a continuum. Many people experience them occasionally or to a minor degree, for example at times of stress, whereas for others they are more intense, enduring and/or distressing.

Although many people find a diagnosis useful, in the arena of mental health diagnostic labels say little about the likely cause of the experiences, and do not appear to describe consistent patterns of problems relating to underlying biological abnormalities.

Introduction: The idea of mental illness

Experiences such as hearing voices or paranoia can sometimes be very distressing, puzzling and worrying, and lead people to seek help. Traditionally, the framework within which help has been offered has been a medical one, and the experiences have been seen as symptoms of mental illnesses, for example schizophrenia. People often assume that mental illnesses 'exist' in the same way that broken bones exist and can be revealed by medical tests in the same way. However, there are many different theories as to what causes experiences such as hearing voices. The idea that they are symptoms of illness, perhaps caused by some sort of chemical imbalance or other problem in the brain, is just one of the theories. There is no objective biological test such as a blood test or scan for diagnosing mental illness.

There is a vigorous debate about whether it is meaningful or useful to think of these experiences as symptoms of mental illnesses. The main issues that are debated are:

- The extent to which psychotic experiences can be separated from normal ones
- The frequency with which 'normal' as well as 'ill' people experience these things
- The extent to which clinicians can agree on someone's diagnosis
- Whether mental illnesses are real 'things'
- The advantages and disadvantages of seeing things as illness.

We will briefly explain each of these in turn.

3.1 Can psychotic experiences be separated from normal ones?

It is often assumed that there is a straightforward dividing line between 'mental health' and 'mental illness' (normality and abnormality) and that discrete, identified disease processes (for example 'schizophrenia') are responsible for experiences such as hearing voices. However, recent research suggests that this is not the case. Viewing experiences as symptoms of illnesses is only one way of seeing them, and one that not everyone finds helpful.

There appears to be a continuum (a continuous line) between good and poor mental health that we all move up and down along at different points in our lives. For example, at different times we may be more or less anxious, suspicious or depressed. At points we probably all also have beliefs that some others would find odd. Stressful life events are likely to have a significant impact on how we think and feel,[1] together with things like how much support we have, and what opportunities we have to make sense of what is happening to us.

The tendency to have certain experiences also varies between individuals as part of a spectrum of complex personal traits and characteristics in the population.[2] On a number of dimensions, people range from being conventionally 'normal' to quite unusual. This 'continuum' view is easily understood by thinking about other common experiences such as anxiety. Individuals differ in terms of how anxious they are in general. This may be an enduring characteristic of their personality, and is likely to involve a combination of genetic factors and upbringing. Only a minority will ever experience extremes of anxiety such as a series of panic attacks, which are recognised in the diagnostic textbooks as justifying a diagnosis of an anxiety disorder. Similarly, the state of extreme suspiciousness known as paranoia is an extension of the feelings of suspiciousness that we all feel from time to time.[3] People differ in this regard: we all know people with whom we have to be very careful what we do or say lest they interpret it as an insult. Similarly, situations vary in their tendency to provoke suspiciousness. We have all been in situations where it makes sense to be extra vigilant, for example walking home alone late at night. In such situations it is easy to be frightened by even the most innocent things.

This 'continuum model' raises questions about traditional psychiatric diagnosis. These are discussed below.

A continuum from 'normality' to 'psychosis'

I felt quite lonely and isolated at school. Even though I had a few friends, I still felt left out and I remember that I started to think that when kids were laughing, that they may have been laughing at me. At the time I knew this was probably wrong, but I couldn't help it, and it started to make me feel even more uncomfortable around school... After university... probably as a result of being isolated again, the thoughts began to come back. However, this time I began to be under the impression that I had some sort of social handicap, similar to autism, and that people could tell this just by the way that I did or didn't make eye contact with them. Consequently, going out on the street became an ordeal because the more self-conscious I felt about my eye contact, the more uncomfortable I felt when looking at people. Eventually, I was convinced that when I was out on the street, everyone who saw me instantly knew I had some sort of social handicap. It actually started to feel as if everybody who met me pretended to treat me normally and then laughed at me behind my back once I'd gone.

Adam [4]

A continuum from 'normality' to 'psychosis' *(continued)*

A 42-year-old divorcee, mother of two children, who has a private practice as a psychic healer, has heard voices 'for as long as she can remember'. She hears the voices via her ears. The voices are located both inside and outside her head. One voice began in childhood and is still present, but she also hears other voices. The initial voice talks to her in the second person. She communicates with this voice, consulting it for the benefit of herself or her clients. Her voices also talk among themselves. Although her voices are not actual voices she has heard in daily life, she is not afraid of them and does not feel restricted by them. Rather, she feels that they are protective: they give her advice, comfort, and care... In her childhood, she was repeatedly physically and sexually abused, and her voices helped her to pull through difficult times... She did not discuss her voices with other people until she was 34. She first talked about her voices with her children after her divorce. She has never been in contact with a psychiatric service, and based on a Composite International Diagnostic Interview with a psychiatrist, she does not fulfil... criteria for a mental disorder.

Marius Romme and Sandra Escher [5]

Well, what can I say? I am starting to believe that I genuinely suffer from one form of paranoia or the other. I started university last year and it has not been entirely easy, academically and socially, although I have encountered feelings of anxiety and paranoia before in my life. If I am with a friend, who maybe has a closer friend with them who does not talk to me as much in the conversation, I always get the feeling that other person does not want me around, or is slightly resentful of my presence. If someone I text does not text back, I assume it is because they do not want to talk to me, and just ignore or delete my text. I also feel they must be annoyed with me for bothering them, and wish I would leave them alone. When I am in shops or on the street, I presume they are watching me to see if I do something strange, so they can secretly laugh to themselves. Or if I have been in a group meeting, as soon as I walk away, they start making comments about how I acted. I also think people are going to make 'look at loner/saddo' expressions when they see me on my own. So, do I suffer from paranoia, and/or low self-esteem? I really want to do something about this, and talk to someone professional who I can trust. But I am even afraid of a professional getting it wrong and putting me on a cocktail of drugs – which I don't want! I would rather talk.

Amber [6]

3.2 Many 'normal' people have unusual experiences

A second finding also casts doubt on the assumption that experiences such as hearing voices are necessarily part of an illness, namely this: such experiences do not appear to be that unusual. Many healthy, well-functioning people sometimes have 'abnormal' experiences. For instance, many people have heard a voice speaking when there was no-one there.[7] Research also suggests that nearly one in three people hold at least one belief that might be considered paranoid: 'paranoia is so common as to be almost normal'.[8]

Only one in 50 of people who have 'psychotic-like' experiences would be classified by doctors as meeting the criteria for a diagnosis of schizophrenia.[9] Extreme circumstances, such as sensory or sleep deprivation, can lead to various disturbances, including paranoia and seeing visions, in people who have never before had such experiences.[10] Some people who hear voices or see visions consider them spiritually enriching.[11, 12, 13] There is huge diversity in the way that experiences are understood in different cultures. For example, cultures and subcultures vary with regard to whether particular experiences are seen as signs of mental illness, as normal (religious and spiritual beliefs, for example), or even as revered spiritual gifts (such as in the case of shamans).[14] These findings suggest that although psychotic experiences can, for some individuals, be extremely distressing and disabling, other people see them as helpful and life enhancing.[15] Of course, for many people they can be both, either at different times or even at the same time: a 'dangerous gift'.[16]

In addition to the finding that psychotic experiences are common and shade into 'normal' ones, a third issue relevant to whether they are best understood as part of an illness is that of 'diagnosis'. The attempt to classify psychological problems using systems of diagnosis has run into problems in three areas: reliability (the extent to which clinicians can agree on a diagnosis), validity (the extent to which the labels refer to real 'things' with common causes) and utility (the extent to which the labels are useful, and to whom).

3.3 Are mental health diagnoses reliable – can clinicians agree?

Reliability is the likelihood that different clinicians will agree upon a diagnosis in any given case. In recent years, much effort has gone into improving reliability, by increasing the number of diagnoses available and by devising 'tick box' type lists of the criteria that have to be met for a particular label to be applied. For example, overleaf are one manual's criteria for making a diagnosis of schizophrenia:

Criteria for a diagnosis of schizophrenia taken from a diagnostic manual (DSM-5)*[17]

All criteria (A – E) must be met:
(See below for an explanation of terms)

A. Characteristics: Two or more of the following, each present for a significant portion of time during a 1-month period (or less if successfully treated). At least one of these must be (1), (2), or (3):

1. Delusions
2. Hallucinations
3. Disorganised speech
4. Grossly disorganised or catatonic** behaviour
5. Negative symptoms (i.e. diminished emotional expression or avolition***)

B. Social/occupational dysfunction: For a significant portion of the time since the onset of the disturbance, level of functioning in one or more major areas, such as work, interpersonal relations, or self-care, is markedly below the level achieved prior to the onset (or when the onset is in childhood or adolescence, there is failure to achieve expected level of interpersonal, academic or occupational functioning).

C. Duration: Continuous signs of the disturbance persist for at least 6 months. This 6-month period must include at least 1 month of symptoms (or less if successfully treated) that meets Criterion A (i.e. active-phase symptoms) and may include periods of prodromal**** or residual symptoms. During these prodromal or residual periods, the signs of the disturbance may be manifested by only negative symptoms or by two or more symptoms listed in Criterion A present in an attenuated form (e.g. odd beliefs, unusual perceptual experiences).

D. Ruling out of other disorders: Schizoaffective disorder and depressive or bipolar disorder with psychotic features have been ruled out because either
1) no depressive or manic episodes have occurred concurrently with the active-phase symptoms, or
2) if mood episodes have occurred during active-phase symptoms, they have been present for a minority of the total duration of the active and residual periods of the illness.

E. Attributes: The disturbance is not attributable to the physiological effects of a substance (e.g. a drug of abuse, a medication) or another medical condition.

F. History: If there is a history of autism spectrum disorder or a communication disorder of childhood onset, the additional diagnosis of schizophrenia is made only if prominent delusions or hallucinations, in addition to the other required symptoms of schizophrenia, are also present for at least a month (or less if successfully treated).

Key:

* The DSM (Diagnostic and Statistical Manual of the American Psychiatric Association) is the American manual, the ICD (International Classification of Diseases) is the international (World Health Organisation) manual. Both are widely used.
** 'catatonic 'means very still and unresponsive
*** 'avolition' means lack of motivation
**** 'prodromal' refers to less severe problems that predate more pronounced problems

Despite these efforts, reliability remains low for most diagnoses, at least in everyday clinical practice where diagnoses are often made without detailed reference to the official manuals.[18] Clinicians tend to have diagnostic 'preferences' and people are often given a range of diagnoses during their contact with mental health services. Research confirms that usage varies between different doctors, hospitals and countries. Even experienced clinicians who have been given extra training in applying the criteria, only agree on a broad diagnostic category about 50 per cent of the time.[19, 20]

I was labelled with all sorts: eating disorder not otherwise specified, major depressive disorder, borderline personality disorder, schizoaffective disorder and eventually schizophrenia… that was the one that knocked the stuffing out of me completely. What was the point in fighting if I was going to be suffering from a lifelong brain disease forever?

Sally Edwards

My psychiatrist gave me various mental health labels… She told me I had what was called 'schizophrenia' by the professionals. However, my mother, who had recently trained as a counsellor and well understood the ramifications of this, was concerned at the possibility of this becoming my diagnosis and the effect this might have on my long-term life prospects. She asked the professionals to reconsider and I was then told I had bipolar, which I later learnt is sometimes seen as being a slightly less (though not always much less) socially damaging diagnosis. I wonder if the professionals would have reconsidered in the way they did, had my mother had less wherewithal to challenge the establishment or had not spoken fluent English? I doubt it.

Raza Griffiths [21]

3.4 Are mental health diagnoses meaningful? Do they refer to real 'things'?

The tendency has always been strong to believe that whatever has a name must be an entity or being, having an independent existence of its own. And if no entity answering to the name could be found, men did not for that reason suppose that none existed, but imagined that it was something peculiarly abstruse and mysterious.

John Stuart Mill (1869) [22]

3.4.1 Naming something doesn't make it real

Experiences such as hearing voices are real experiences for the person having them, and can lead to very real distress. However, this does not mean that they are necessarily symptoms of real 'illnesses', for example schizophrenia. Giving something a name, and even being very clear about its definition, doesn't mean that it necessarily exists in reality. Most people would agree on how to identify a unicorn, for example, even though they are mythical rather than real creatures. The problem is that the existence of the label can give the misleading impression of the existence of the 'thing'. As psychiatrist Jim Van Os puts it: 'The complicated, albeit ultimately meaningless, Greek term suggests that schizophrenia really is a "thing", i.e. a "brain disease" that exists as such in Nature. This is a false suggestion.'[23] The extent to which a label refers to a meaningful entity in the real world is sometimes called 'validity'. Dr Thomas Insel, Director of the National Institute of Mental Health in the US, is critical of the current diagnostic approach: 'Patients deserve better. The weakness is its lack of validity.'[24] So to be clear: the experiences and distress are very real, but the explanation – that there is an illness called 'schizophrenia' causing them – may not be true.

3.4.2 What a diagnostic label does not tell you
We normally expect medical diagnoses to tell us something about what has caused a certain problem, what the person can expect in future ('prognosis') and what is likely to help. However, this is not the case with mental health 'diagnoses', which rather than being explanations are just ways of categorising experiences based on what people tell clinicians. The *Diagnostic and Statistical Manual of the American Psychiatric Association* (DSM) explicitly states that its categories say nothing about cause – in its own words it is 'neutral with respect to theories of aetiology'.[25] For example, someone who says that they are hearing voices might be given a diagnosis of schizophrenia. Since this says nothing about cause, it makes little sense to say that the person hears the voices 'because of' the schizophrenia. An analogy with physical medicine might be a label such as 'idiopathic pain', which merely means that a person is reporting pain, but a cause of that pain cannot be identified. Turning to 'prognosis', as we explain below outcome is very variable. In terms of what can help, the same drugs and psychological therapies are used for a range of diagnoses, and two people with the same diagnosis often find very different things helpful. This suggests that diagnostic categories do not reflect 'real' categories or differences between people: they don't 'carve nature at the joints'.[26]

3.4.3 Experiences are on a continuum and don't fall into neat categories
Another relevant finding is the one mentioned above, namely that many people hear voices or hold beliefs that others regard as bizarre, but do not have a diagnosis and would not meet the criteria for one.[27] Whereas the traditional view has been that some people have an illness (a 'thing' called psychosis or schizophrenia), and others don't, as we explained above; a more helpful and accurate view is probably to see experiences as on a continuum (a line joining two ends of a scale). People who rarely have such experiences, or who find them helpful, might be at one end of the continuum. At the other end would be those who have very frequent, intense and distressing experiences. Some of these people might need considerable help and support, and some see themselves as ill. This approach underlies a recent initiative to classify problems for research purposes, the 'Research Domain Criteria' (RDoC).[28] This attempts to develop a new system of classification based on measuring various things which are each continuous, but might affect the likelihood of someone experiencing problems, for example how quickly they tend to become emotionally aroused or to calm down.

3.4.4 The ever-expanding reach of mental health diagnoses

Over time, the list of psychiatric diagnoses has grown and grown, and some have argued that the list is now so exhaustive that we would all fit one category or other. This is one reason that the newest version of the diagnostic manual, DSM 5, has been so controversial.[29] The diagnosis of schizophrenia is particularly so. For example, there is evidence that young black men are particularly likely to receive a diagnosis of schizophrenia and that this might relate partly to racism (and perhaps also gender and class discrimination) both in society and within services.[30,31,32,33] Dr Jonathan Metzl points out that there was in the past even a specific diagnosis of 'negro schizophrenia' and that in the 1960s many young men taking part in the civil rights movement were labelled with 'protest psychosis'.[34,35] Professor Suman Fernando has pointed out that 'excessive labelling with schizophrenia links up with excessive stop and search, prison, and school exclusion'.[36]

3.4.5 Has the idea of schizophrenia arisen as a result of the 'Clinician's Illusion'?

Evidence is accumulating that the idea of an illness called schizophrenia might be the result of clinicians experiencing a phenomenon called 'Berkson's Bias' [37,38] – in other words, concluding that two things are related when in fact, they both independently affect the likelihood of someone seeking help from services. For example, many people sometimes experience one or more of the following: finding it hard to look after themselves, feeling desperate, confused or disoriented, hearing voices, thinking suspicious or paranoid thoughts. There is increasing evidence that, contrary to what clinicians have traditionally believed, these experiences are often unrelated.[39] Those who experience only one or two of these problems are unlikely to seek help from services. Only people who experience several of them and to a severe degree, are likely to end up seeking help from services and so receive a diagnosis.[40, 41] This is what underlies the so-called 'clinician's illusion',[42] namely the idea that people who have one of these experiences (hearing voices, say) also tend to have many of the others, to be very distressed, and to have ongoing problems.

3.5 The advantages and disadvantages of seeing things as mental illness

The previous sections suggest that the 'illness' view does not always accord with what we know from science. It is certainly clear that it is only one way of understanding experiences such as hearing voices, rather than the only way. So the question arises: is it the most helpful way?

Thinking of things as an illness can have some advantages. It gives us a way of talking about difficult things and a framework for offering help: time off work with sick pay or benefits if needed, and access to services. For people involved in planning services or efforts at prevention, diagnoses provide a way of talking about groups of people when we are looking at where and when certain problems tend to occur, or what might help. They are also currently used in decisions about allocation of resources in health services. Some people welcome a diagnosis because it implies that they are not alone in what they are experiencing.[43] Some are concerned that if others don't see them as ill, they might blame them (or perhaps their family) for their problems and see them as lacking in willpower or determination to get over them. This has been called the 'blame or brain' dilemma and is addressed below.[44]

People who find a diagnosis helpful and think of themselves as having an illness

I think I prefer my illness having a name because it makes me feel less lonely, and I know that there are other people experiencing my kind of misery. And that people live through my illness and make a meaningful existence with it. But I also have to be careful not to adopt the sick role, since I know I would just give up if I did that.

Karin Falk [45]

When someone confronts you with the line 'you're ill' it's easy to reject it out of hand and dismiss it totally. But denial can be extremely damaging. I see my first six years in the system as being in limbo. Acceptance of my illness was a turning point – the start of my path to wellness. It is important to understand that denial of the illness can be a natural reaction and a normal defence mechanism to a very painful truth. Society has a dim view of mental illness and the stigma around it is very powerful. For me, denial was my way of coping, of staying normal. It was a way of dealing with the initial trauma of breaking down. The trouble with not accepting is that you also reject treatment. You refuse medication, fight confinement and rebel, or worse – turn on those trying to help you. This behaviour gets you nowhere, and just makes things worse. By accepting treatment I could actively seek the right medication, access support, and turn my life around. Without acceptance you remain trapped in the delusion that nothing's wrong. I've seen many stuck there – a bad place to be.

Terry Bowyer [46]

There is a point where it becomes what we call an illness – we don't function properly and we are experiencing very unusual things and reacting very unusually... The problem lies ... in what we attach to the ideas of illness. If the concept of illness was extended from biology to include our emotional/spiritual/thinking and meaning-making faculties we would have a holistic approach which would offer more.

Laura Lea, Contributor

However, in other ways thinking in terms of illness can be unhelpful. Some people feel that, overall, the idea of mental illness does more harm than good. Interviews with people who had been given a diagnosis of psychosis suggested that many felt labelled in society as a 'mental patient' or 'schizophrenic'. They felt that the diagnosis had disempowered them and led to them being excluded from mainstream society.[47] Similarly, a review concluded that being seen as mentally ill causes more distress for many people than their original problems.[48] People seen as mentally ill are often avoided, treated harshly and subject to discrimination.[49] For example, although having a job can be very important in people's recovery, employers are less likely to offer work to someone if they know that they have a psychiatric diagnosis[50] and unemployment rates for people with a 'psychotic' diagnosis are very high.[51] Reviews of the available evidence[52] suggest that viewing distress as 'an illness like any other' can actually increase prejudice and discrimination.[53] Some writers have suggested that presenting problems as an illness has the effect of making them seem mysterious and unpredictable, and the people experiencing the problems as 'almost another species'.[54]

Receiving a diagnosis can also have negative psychological effects on the person, for example leading to feelings of hopelessness and decreased confidence. It can give the message that people can do little to overcome their problems except to 'keep taking the tablets'. It can divert attention from the possible meaning or positive aspects that the experiences might have for the person.[55] It can also deflect attention away from underlying social and emotional problems that could otherwise be addressed in a restorative way, for example the aftermath of adversities like poverty, discrimination, childhood abuse or assault.[56] Importantly, the way that diagnoses appear to summarise the nature and causes of someone's experience can prevent workers from asking about, and helping, the person to deal with the events and emotions that may in reality underlie the problems.

People who find 'diagnoses' unhelpful and do not think of themselves as having an illness

For a number of years, I accepted the medical model as a framework of understanding...
But I gradually came to appreciate drawbacks to the framework. My reading suggested the model might not stand up scientifically. The emphasis on distress as illness not only encouraged a resort to exclusively physical treatments (drugs, ECT) but pushed to one side any consideration of the content and meaning of my crisis episodes. Thinking of myself as having a chronic and incurable illness robbed me of power and agency and confined me within an essentially negative category. By the time I was entering my second decade of service use, the medical model, which I had initially found reassuring, seemed increasingly unsatisfactory, without the capacity to encompass the complexity of my interior or exterior life and give it positive value. As a result, I began to actively explore frameworks that better met my needs.

Peter Campbell [57]

I was told I had a disease... I was beginning to undergo that radically dehumanising and devaluing transformation ... from being Pat Deegan to being 'a schizophrenic'.

Pat Deegan [58]

Maybe (my) sensitivity to criticism is because being given a diagnosis is like a kick in the teeth. They're not saying that there's something wrong with your liver, but that something is wrong with you.

Anon [59]

My diagnosis of 'schizophrenia' was changed by my psychiatrist because of my persistence, of not acknowledging the diagnosis. I think the issue was that I was angry towards the psychiatrist for not acknowledging my cultural knowledge or way of life.

Odi Oquosa [60]

Once past the 'relief response' on learning a name for the distress – the label itself does not alleviate the pain. It does not help the professional or the individual to understand what is happening or what would assist the individual. It stops the individual from owning the experience and finding his/her own language and interpretation ... the labelled people are seen as inferior or less competent... People become dependent and helpless with the treatments and labels.

Louise Pembroke [61]

I am labelled for the rest of my life...I think schizophrenia will always make me a second class citizen... I haven't got a future.

Henry [62]

3.6 Recent recommendations to move away from using diagnoses

In view of the problems with diagnoses, many researchers and clinicians are moving away from using them, and recent high-profile reports have recommended this.[63, 64]

After an extensive review of the evidence, the Schizophrenia Commission, despite its name, advocated 'extreme caution in making a diagnosis of schizophrenia as it can generate stigma and unwarranted pessimism'.[65] There is an ongoing 'Inquiry into the Schizophrenia Label' (www.schizophreniainquiry.org) which has reported that many people feel that they have been harmed by being given the diagnosis. Many felt that it had caused them more distress than their original difficulties.[66]

The British Psychological Society (BPS) has stated that 'clients and the general public are negatively affected by the continued and continuous medicalisation of their natural and normal responses to their experiences; responses which undoubtedly have distressing consequences ... but which do not reflect illnesses so much as normal individual variation... This misses the relational context of problems and the undeniable social causation of many such problems'.[67] The BPS Division of Clinical Psychology (DCP) has explicitly criticised the current systems of psychiatric diagnosis such as DSM–5 and ICD–10.[68, 69] It has suggested that we need 'a paradigm shift in relation to the experiences that these diagnoses refer to, towards a conceptual system not based on a 'disease' model'.[70]

This suggestion has attracted widespread support and a 'Global Summit on Diagnostic Alternatives' has been set up.[71] The DCP has suggested one alternative for use in clinical practice: an approach called 'collaborative formulation'[72] which is described in Section 8 of this report. Formulations explore the personal meaning of the events, relationships and social circumstances of someone's life, and of their current experiences or distress. The person experiencing the difficulty works together with the professional to develop a hypothesis, or best guess, which can provide a basis for finding a way forward.[73] Unlike a diagnosis, formulation is based on the assumption that however extreme, unusual or overwhelming the nature of that distress '...at some level it all makes sense'.[74] Formulations are an answer to the 'brain or blame' dilemma mentioned above: they make sense of problems in a way that neither implies that people are to blame, nor that their problems are 'all in the mind'. As we will go on to discuss, a huge range of factors contribute to distress, and there are no simple causes. Each person's problems, and the causes of their problems, are different. Perhaps the analogy of poverty is helpful – all kinds of people find themselves in financial difficulty, for all kinds of reasons. We wouldn't diagnose an 'illness' of poverty, we wouldn't assume that the causes are the same in every case, and we wouldn't assume that people are always to blame for their financial troubles. Each case is different, each case is a serious problem that needs to be understood and responded to, but neither 'diagnosis' nor blame is appropriate.

Section 4: How do these experiences affect people's lives?

Key points:

There is huge variability in people's experiences: whilst some people find their experiences very distressing, others are relatively untroubled by them and some people even experience them as positive.

Whilst some people have distressing and disabling experiences for many years, many others experience psychosis only once in their lives, often at a time of particular stress.

Even if people continue to hear voices or hold unusual beliefs, they may nevertheless lead very happy and successful lives. Sometimes a tendency to 'psychosis' can be associated with particular talents or abilities.

The idea that psychosis often leads to violence is a myth.

The variability in how people's experiences affect them makes it vital for mental health services to address all aspects of people's wellbeing rather than just attempting to reduce 'symptoms'.

4.1 Variability in outcomes

As mentioned above, many people who hear voices or see visions – perhaps two out of three – are not troubled by them and do not seek help from mental health services.[1] Even for those whose experiences are distressing and lead to contact with services, the outlook is much better than is commonly assumed. About half will experience problems on one occasion only and then recover completely. Only a minority experience on-going difficulties:[2] for those people, of course, it is vital that long-term, open-ended, high-quality support is available. Outcomes also vary between countries.[3] A recent review concluded that 'the idea that schizophrenia is a progressive brain disease is not supported by the weight of longitudinal neuroimaging and cognitive studies... [this idea] has contributed to undue pessimism among mental health professionals.'[4]

> I work four days a week in a professional job; I own my own house and live happily with my partner and pets. Occasionally I hear voices – for example when I have been particularly stressed or tired, or I have seen visions after a bereavement. Knowing that many people hear voices and live well, and that some cultures see these experiences as a gift, helps me to never catastrophise or to worry that it may be the start of a breakdown. Although I am lucky that the experiences have never been as upsetting as some people's, if someone had told me it was madness I could have got into a vicious cycle and struggled to get out.
>
> Sara

4.2 Which outcomes matter?

> Recovery is about building a meaningful and satisfying life, as defined by the person themselves, whether or not there are ongoing or recurring symptoms or problems.
>
> Geoff Shepherd, Jed Boardman & Mike Slade [5]

Outcome is a complex phenomenon. Things might improve for someone – or remain difficult – on a number of dimensions that could be relatively independent of each other.[6] Examples might include:

- 'Clinical' outcome – whether or not someone continues to have the particular distressing experiences or symptoms.
- 'Personal' outcome – the extent to which someone is able to make meaningful sense of their experience in a way that others can respect, and to find a way of integrating the experiences into their life. The extent to which their distress reduces and they are satisfied with their life.
- 'Social' outcome – the extent to which someone has valued roles within their community and has good housing, income and relationships.

People who continue to have severe and distressing experiences may lead happy and successful lives in all other respects, such as work and relationships. Many people find that the hardest part of recovery is overcoming prejudice, discrimination, lowered expectations and the pressure to subscribe to a 'sick role'.[7] This can be particularly hard for people who in addition to experiencing psychosis are also members of devalued or disadvantaged groups in terms of ethnicity, gender, sexual preference, age or social class.[8] A Mental Health Foundation study suggested for example that 'recovery approaches focusing on getting black women back into employment and education are not going to be effective unless they are also equipped to deal with the oppressions that they face in society'.[9]

The important outcomes are those that the person themselves sees as significant. 'Getting better' means different things to different people; for some, reducing the frequency or intensity of the experiences is most important, but for others it is other things – improved relationships, confidence, self-worth, greater engagement in work and activities, being able to cope with everyday life, material wellbeing, physical health,[10] hope for the future and a sense of purpose.[11] It is important that measures of outcome capture these aspects as well as reduction in 'symptoms'.[12, 13]

4.3 Influences on outcome

Five processes appear to be particularly important for recovery and wellbeing: connecting to the world outside of oneself (e.g. supportive relationships, spirituality), hope, a positive identity beyond being a patient, finding meaning in life, and empowerment (learning what helps and so gaining control, and having the right opportunities).[14, 15]

About a psychiatrist

I would talk of how I was,
My application for jobs,
My art work,
My sleep, depression,
My inability to work consistently...
He would listen, ask questions, and comment,
...Open-minded to treatment –
Psychiatry is not an exact science –
New ideas,
New alternatives were not rejected.
He realised the missing,
The search for status,
He kept up my hope.

R. Lilly [16]

Recovery rates are better during periods of full employment compared with periods of economic recession.[17] People who find work tend to do better,[18] especially when they choose the work and have control over it, when it uses their skills and is valued by others.[19,20] Encountering prejudice and discrimination, either on mental health grounds or on other grounds such as ethnicity, class, gender or sexuality can also be a significant obstacle to recovery.[21,22] Additionally, regardless of affluence, more people experience mental health problems in countries where the gap between rich and poor is greatest.[23] Again, this suggests that being valued by others, feeling (and being treated as) equal to those around you and having control over your own life are important.[24]

People who have supportive relationships tend to do better than those who have less support or more stressful relationships.[25, 26] In particular, people tend to do less well if their partners or family members are highly critical or overprotective.[27]

Sam's story

Sam first heard distressing voices in her teens after being raped. She coped by using illegal drugs. She came to the attention of services after hitting the man who had raped her. She found hope through reading other people's recovery stories, making sense of her own experiences and taking control of her life. She and others believed in her recovery and focused on her strengths, and she was able to take advantage of work opportunities that arose. She wrote about her story so that readers could gain hope and progress with their own recovery journey. Hers has continued and she has not used medication or mental health services for ten years.

It was awful. I had problems and a very long history. I was in hospital for 12 years – six different places – from 17 years old. They diagnosed me with so many things – personality disorder, paranoia, schizophrenia. They pumped me full of drugs. They used to say you will never get out. My recovery started when I went into assertive outreach and started seeing the psychologist. It was hard work – horrible sometimes. What I needed was to sit down and make sense of what was going on in my head. I've spent hardly any time in hospital since.

I got a job. Work has helped me. It's given me confidence to know I could do this.

Sam

4.4 The myth that psychosis leads to violence

In contrast to media stereotypes, in reality few people who experience paranoia or hear distressing voices ever hurt anyone else. It is very slightly more common for people with psychiatric diagnoses to commit violent crimes than for those without such diagnoses. However, the difference in rates is extremely small: far less, for example, than the increased risk associated with any one of: being male, being young, having consumed alcohol or used street drugs, or having been violent in the past.[28] It is also possible that even the slight apparent difference is actually due to the fact that people who have been violent are more likely than others to come into contact with the authorities and therefore to be assessed and receive a diagnosis. Most violence is committed by people who have never been in contact with mental health services and the overwhelming majority of mental health service users have never been violent.[29, 30] In those cases where somebody with a history of using mental health services is violent, the usual risk factors for violence (gender, alcohol or drug use, a past history of violent behaviour) are usually more important factors to consider than the mental health issues. Moreover, specific diagnoses like schizophrenia do not predict dangerousness.[31] The reason that people associate a diagnosis with violence is most likely a result of negative and stereotyped media reporting about mental health.[32] A survey found that homicide and crime were the most frequent themes in media coverage of mental health.[33] Films and television dramas also often depict people with mental health problems as violent and unpredictable.[34, 35] However, as a result of people's fear and prejudice, mental health service users are much more likely than others to be *victims* of violence.[36]

This is particularly the case for black service users, who can sometimes experience double discrimination. Both the public and mental health professionals are prone to overestimating the likelihood that young black men in particular will be violent.[37,38,39,40] As a result they often get a very poor deal from services and are more likely than others to be locked up or medicated against their will.[41,42,43,44,45] One result can be a 'circle of fear'[46,47] where people are afraid of services, avoid them even in times of crisis, and are then even more likely to experience coercion, for example being 'sectioned' under the Mental Health Act.

Part 2: Causes

Why do so many people have these experiences and when do they become distressing?

Introduction to Part 2

As with other human characteristics, there is an ongoing debate about what causes the tendency to have 'psychotic' experiences. Life events and circumstances, inherited tendencies and the way we see the world and interpret events can all play a role. It's important to bear in mind that the 'causes' of complex human thoughts and feelings are different from the 'causes' of simpler things such as chemical reactions. We need to be careful in the way we think here. In particular, although there are commonalities, different combinations of causes are likely to be relevant for different people, and to interact with each other. There is no 'one size fits all' explanation. Different people experience these things for different reasons. People who have themselves experienced psychosis hold a variety of views about the nature and causes of their difficulties.[1] Since no professional is in a position to know for sure exactly which elements combined together to cause problems for a particular person, it is important to respect people's own views.

An enormous range of things have been proposed as possible causes of psychotic experiences.[2] As every thought is both a brain-based event and a human experience, it can be impossible to separate out different types of causes. It can be helpful to think in terms of 'levels of explanation' rather than causes. For example, a thought can be explained in terms of its brain chemistry (which chemicals are involved?), its psychology (e.g. do people have different 'thinking styles' in different moods?) or its social context (e.g. what has happened to which the thought is a reaction?). An explanation might link these levels but one does not 'cause' the other any more than, say, the wiring of a television 'causes' the plot of EastEnders. We need to understand many different things in order to explain why people spend hours watching a flickering screen.

Traditionally, the search for causes of psychosis has focused mainly on genetics and on aspects of brain structure and functioning. Psychologists have also looked at the way that people interpret information and their 'thinking styles'. More recently, research has focused on how both of these aspects might relate to the circumstances of people's lives and things that have happened to them. Over the last 15 years or so, we have discovered much more about the role that life events can play for many people, particularly deprivation and trauma. It seems that, as with other problems such as anxiety and depression, a major cause of many psychotic experiences lies in things that have happened in people's lives, and how these have affected them.

Section 5: Biology – our brains

Key points

Every human experience has biological, psychological and social aspects. Experiences such as hearing voices or holding unusual beliefs are the result of complex interactions between the circumstances of our lives, the way we see the world and interpret events, and our biological makeup.

For each person, there will be a different pattern of causes: for some people, constitutional factors will play a significant role, whereas for others the most important causes will be the circumstances and events of their lives.

There is a constant interaction between these different aspects of our experiences, so it doesn't make sense to look for a single cause of any experience.

To date we do not have firm evidence for any specific biological mechanism underlying psychotic experiences.

Introduction

It is widely assumed that psychosis has a biological cause. It is in pharmaceutical companies' interests to promote the idea that schizophrenia is a brain disease: Eli Lilly's website states that 'schizophrenia is a ... neurological disorder, believed to be caused by a biochemical imbalance in the brain'.[1] Although often reported uncritically by the media, this view is hotly debated.[2] It has been subject to increasing challenge over recent years, as it has become clear that our experiences, our psychology and our biological make-up all play a role, and all affect each other. The precise combination of causes will be different for each person. No professional can ever say with certainty what has caused one particular individual to have certain experiences. Biological factors can play their part, and there are clearly cases where they are important, for example when someone has a psychotic experience when they are physically ill or have taken particular drugs.

However, despite all the research that has been done, there is still little or no evidence that for the majority of people, a problem in the brain can be considered the main cause of psychotic experiences, or that there is a brain disease called schizophrenia. Many neurological and biochemical pathways in the brain are likely to be involved in experiences such as hearing voices. However, this is also the case for all other human experiences. For example, our brain chemistry is different when we are happy from when we are sad. 'Cause' can also work both ways: chemical changes in the brain could lead us to see the world differently, but equally things that happen to us can cause changes in the brain. The undoubted existence of biological aspects to distressing experiences does not in itself tell us anything about what causes them, or justify categorising them as brain diseases.

5.1 Genetics

The tendency to hear voices or hold unusual beliefs sometimes 'runs in families' and, as with other characteristics and experiences, genetics can certainly play a role. However, the methodology and results of studies relating to genetic factors in 'schizophrenia' are the subject of much debate in professional journals.[3, 4, 5, 6, 7] It is impossible completely to disentangle genetics from environmental factors such as upbringing and life circumstances (in other words to separate 'nature' from 'nurture').

Research looking at the possible role of genetics often compares identical and non-identical twins, or biological and adoptive relatives of people who have been given a diagnosis of schizophrenia. Current research also uses a technique called 'GWAS'[8] or 'genome-wide association study'. This technique is most often used in the field of physical health to look more precisely at genetic differences between people with or without a particular disease.

These techniques have identified certain genetic characteristics that appear to be more common among people who have certain mental health diagnoses.[9] Such research is sometimes heralded in the media as a breakthrough[10] which might one day 'uncover the genetic basis of mental disorders'.[11] However, we need to interpret such claims with caution. The genetic similarities which the studies identify are associated not with one 'disorder' but with a wide range of characteristics, for example the tendency to be emotional, or problems with concentration. We should remember that genes code for proteins, not experiences. For some people they can play an important role, but only as part (perhaps 6 per cent, according to one recent study[12]) of the complex web of interacting factors that contribute to a particular experience. That is very different to the claim sometimes made that 'schizophrenia is a genetic disorder'.

Whilst in the past researchers were looking for a causal gene, it now appears that genetic risk is much less specific. There may be many heritable characteristics which each increase the likelihood of someone experiencing psychosis if they are exposed to particular life events. An example might be a sensitive temperament. In many circumstances sensitivity is of course a good thing,[13] but all else being equal, people who are particularly sensitive might be more likely to experience psychosis if they experience hardship, abuse or trauma.[14]

Another new and interesting area of research concerns 'epigenetics'. This is the study of how parts of our genetic mechanisms are 'switched on', 'turned up' or 'turned down' by the things that happen in our lives. So, for instance, a gene that is responsible for the production of a specific protein may be more or less active, so produce more or less of that protein, in different environmental conditions. The gene is still there, but it may be more or less active depending on the environment.

In summary: when we are trying to understand any one person's experience, genetics might be one part of the jigsaw. But because the genetic elements of this jigsaw are common to many different experiences, and also interact with environmental factors, it doesn't make sense to single out them out as 'the' cause, or even the most important one.

5.2 Neurochemical theories

It is often suggested that psychosis might be caused by an imbalance or difference in brain chemicals (neurotransmitters). Some evidence for this argument comes from the effects of drugs. Firstly, people who use a lot of cannabis appear to be more at risk of developing psychosis,[15] although it is not always easy to separate the effects of the drug from the circumstances that may have led people to seek solace in drug use in the first place. Secondly, neuroleptic medication, which can 'dampen down' experiences such as hearing voices, also affects neurotransmitters. Further evidence comes from brain imaging studies, which suggest that there might be differences in the way some chemicals behave in the brains of some people who have been diagnosed with schizophrenia.[16] There are over 100 neurotransmitters in the brain, but so far researchers have concentrated on three: dopamine, serotonin and glutamate.

The dopamine hypothesis – the theory that psychosis may result from differences in the way the brain produces and handles the neurotransmitter dopamine – is often put forward as a biochemical explanation. This suggestion has been extensively researched over the last 30 years, and three types of evidence have been put forward in support of it. Firstly, some brain imaging studies using injections of a dopamine-related chemical have suggested that there may be differences in the way the chemical behaves in the brains of some people with a diagnosis of schizophrenia when compared to people without a diagnosis.[17] Secondly, many neuroleptic ('anti-psychotic') drugs are thought to affect dopamine.[18] These drugs can sometimes induce Parkinsonism – abnormal movements similar to those seen in Parkinson's disease. Parkinsonism is known to be related to problems with dopamine mechanisms. Thirdly, drugs such as amphetamines, which increase dopamine production, can also produce psychotic-like experiences.

Some of the newer neuroleptics affect a different neurotransmitter – serotonin. Research into the possible role of serotonin,[19] and other neurotransmitters such as glutamate,[20] has so far been inconclusive.[21]

It is important to remember that the function of all neurotransmitters is to convey information. Dopamine, for example, is used in the pathway which communicates social threat or fear. It would therefore be surprising if it were not involved in the experience of, say, paranoid anxiety. We do not yet know the details of these kinds of mechanisms, but it is at least plausible to suggest that differences between people in terms of their brain chemicals, might be at least partly a result of different life experiences which have led certain pathways to be more active. So even if a reliable relationship were found between a biochemical characteristic and a particular experience, for example hearing voices, this would not necessarily tell us anything about cause and effect. It may be the case that the experience leads to biochemical changes rather than the other way around. It is also possible that some third factor, for example the medication that people are taking, might be responsible. Our knowledge of the biochemistry of psychotic experiences (and indeed of the biochemistry of most other forms of human experience) is very limited, and we are not in a position to make any firm statements about biochemical causes. The complex jigsaw of factors involved in experiences such as hearing voices inevitably involves brain chemicals, but it is important to remember that they are only one part of the jigsaw rather than 'the' cause.

5.3 Brain structure and function

Research has also examined the possible role of brain structure and function.[22] For example, recent brain imaging studies have examined patterns of blood flow and electrical activity in the brain.[23]

Some studies have found differences in structure (e.g. volume of 'grey matter' in certain areas) and function (e.g. more or fewer signals appearing to pass between different areas) when average results from a group of people with a diagnosis of schizophrenia are compared with those from a group of people without the diagnosis. Some of these differences, for example in the size of structures known as the hippocampus and amygdala, appear to pre-date formal diagnosis.[24] However, these findings need to be interpreted with caution for a number of reasons:

- There is always a big overlap between the groups – it is not possible to look at someone's results and say with confidence whether or not they have experienced psychosis.

- Most studies compare groups of people with and without a diagnosis of schizophrenia. If, as suggested above, 'diagnosis' is inherently problematic in this area, then arguably we can conclude little from comparing these two groups. As we explained above, people who end up receiving a diagnosis, using services for a significant time, and being included in research studies are often those who have difficulties or needs in a number of areas. They are not typical of everyone who has psychotic experiences such as voice hearing.

- In most studies the people with a history of 'psychosis' have also taken powerful medication for many years. Recent evidence suggests that this can cause changes in the structure of the brain, for example a reduction in its overall size.[25]

- Finally, it is important to remember that life experiences, distress and trauma may themselves leave physical traces on the brain, as well as the other way round. A striking example of this is the finding that physical changes can be seen in an area of the brain called the hippocampus[26] as London taxi-drivers learn 'the knowledge', building up their mental map of the streets of the capital. Recent research has suggested that the reason for any differences in the brains of people who experience 'psychosis' might often be early traumatic events in their lives, rather than differences that they were born with.[27, 28] For example, the 'social defeat theory of schizophrenia'[29] suggests that repeated experiences of being disadvantaged and socially excluded can lead to sensitivity in the dopamine pathways in the brain.[30]

A complete list of all the factors that have been identified as potential causes of psychosis would cover every aspect of biological functioning. However, there is no conclusive evidence that biological abnormalities are the main cause of this or indeed any other mental health problem. As the chair of the task force that produced DSM-5[31] (a widely used diagnostic manual) stated: 'In the future, we hope to be able to identify disorders using biological and genetic markers... we've been telling patients for several decades that we are waiting for biomarkers [a measurable characteristic indicative of a particular disease]. We're still waiting.'[32]

5.4 Conclusions

For some of us, aspects of our biological makeup appear to contribute to the likelihood that we will have an experience such as hearing voices. However this does not necessarily imply that we should think of psychosis as a biological illness. Despite decades of research, no specific biological mechanism has been identified as the main cause of psychotic experiences. The relevant aspects of someone's biological makeup are likely to be more general, for example a sensitive constitution. Whilst biological factors might be very important for some people, for others they may play little if any role: for example, we might all have psychotic experiences if subject to certain types of stress. As with other complex human experiences, there are many 'causes': our biological makeup constantly interacts with both our personal characteristics and our environment. The complex reasons for one person's experiences may have little in common with the causes of someone else's.

However, the widespread acceptance of the idea that diagnoses such as schizophrenia refer to biological illnesses has led to a situation where people often assume that experiences such as hearing voices always arise from a problem within the brain. As a result workers have often not tried to understand the experiences in the context of the person's life, or prioritised talking to the person about their experiences. The 'brain disease' idea has also contributed to a climate in which the main, or only, treatment tends to be medication. This in turn has meant that other approaches to helping, such as talking treatments, have often been unavailable. It has also diverted resources away from the circumstances of people's lives, not only in the way that we try to help people in distress, but also in research and in efforts at prevention.[33, 34]

Section 6: Life experiences and how they affect us

Key points

The role that life experiences can play is becoming clearer. Psychosis can often be a response to the things that happen in our lives, particularly traumatic or very stressful events.

People who are poor or live in unequal societies are more likely than others to develop mental health problems. Psychosis is no exception.

Introduction

Over recent years it has become clear that psychosis can sometimes be a response to the things that happen in our lives, particularly traumatic events. In other words:
'Bad things happen and can drive you crazy'.[1]

6.1 Life events and trauma

We all deal with many stressful events in our lives – divorce, rejection, redundancy, bitter disappointments, bereavement and various kinds of failure. Even positive events – winning the lottery, for example – can be stressful. Some of us have more than most to deal with, in the shape of poverty, bullying, family problems, loneliness, abuse or trauma. Those of us from black and minority ethnic (BME) backgrounds often experience ongoing and routine racism, insults and discrimination, the effects of which can build up over time[2] until things reach a crisis point. Some of us have been traumatised by warfare or torture or have experienced great hardship as refugees.[3,4] Much evidence has now accumulated to suggest that, like other mental health problems, 'psychosis' can be a reaction to such stressful events and life circumstances, particularly abuse or other forms of trauma.[5,6] For example, voices may relate to previous events which have left difficult feelings and memories that need to be explored and resolved. All communities remember their history, and sometimes people's experiences (voices, for example) echo past forms of persecution such as slavery. A review found that between half and three-quarters of psychiatric inpatients had been either physically or sexually abused as children.[7] Experiencing multiple childhood traumas appears to give approximately the same risk of developing psychosis as smoking does for developing lung cancer.[8]

Often the content of people's experiences is related to the nature of the trauma. For example, a survivor of childhood abuse struggling with negative feelings about themselves might hear the voice of a former abuser telling them they are worthless, and this might further reinforce their low self-esteem. Trauma survivors are often troubled by flashbacks and intrusive images, or may 'dissociate' – mentally leave the situation, cut off or 'blank out'. Many refugees hear voices or experience visions related to the traumas they have been through.[9] It is becoming clear that there is much more overlap than was previously thought between these trauma-related experiences and those that have been thought of as psychosis.[10] This overlap is currently the focus of much research,[11, 12, 13] and an editorial in the *British Journal of Psychiatry* has suggested that 'the implications of our having finally taken seriously the causal role of childhood adversity are profound'.[14] Some psychologists are reaching the conclusion that psychosis is often no more and no less than a natural reaction to traumatic events. For example one recent paper suggested that 'there is growing evidence that the experiences service users report ... are, in many cases, a natural reaction to the abuses they have been subjected to. There is abuse and there are the effects of abuse. There is no additional 'psychosis' that needs explaining'.[15]

Life events

After being almost killed by my ex-boyfriend when I was 16 I have had OCD. I have also developed paranoia about someone trying to kill me. If I have conflict with someone over anything I worry they are going to kill me or have someone come and kill me. I wake up worried someone is in my bedroom. I think about trying to be ready to protect myself if someone comes at me. I don't think I would have this if I had not been traumatised half my life ago.

Josephine [16]

When I was a child we lived on an all-white road. Nobody was friendly to us and, as luck would have it, our next door neighbour was a member of the National Front and he kept throwing abuse over the garden wall at us... It was really horrible, horrible stuff. And when you were growing up as a child, you think that's how the outside world sees you. You are not going to have pride in yourself and you actually fear the world around you. I can see where that has had a knock-on effect on my experience of paranoia.

Anon [17]

I thought I was bad because the voices called me all sorts of names. Later I realised that the voices were related to the physical abuse because they have the characteristics of those that abused me. Then I noticed that the voices became more or less intrusive depending on the situation I was in. They became bad when there were conflicts in the house. So they were a kind of mirror of my living situation.

Daan Marsman [18]

Having gone through an abusive childhood – physical, verbal, mental and sexual – I have suffered with severe depression now for over 10 years. Recently, following the breakup of my marriage, I have started having paranoid thoughts. I constantly feel that I am being followed when I am driving the car. I have taken alternative routes to evade my followers and on one occasion really believed my abusive parents were following me. At other times it is the Social Services. I constantly have these thoughts and at the time cannot justify them, become anxious, panicky and afraid. Only after can I calm down and quantify them. I also have had paranoid thoughts about people coming into my garden, re-arranging the plant pots, etc. and my home where I have thought someone has been in and moved something. When they are happening I go completely crazy and have even hit myself to make the thoughts go away. Sometimes I feel that I am losing my mind completely. My doctor has now put me on Olanzapine and they are somewhat easier to handle but still frighten me and make me feel confused and violated.

Janice [19]

6.2 Relationships

As we said earlier, no professional is in a position to say with certainty what has caused a particular person to experience psychosis at a particular point in their life. This is particularly important in the area of family relationships. In the past, family members have sometimes felt blamed. Since as we said above, no-one knows for sure all the reasons that a particular problem might have arisen, it is very important that professionals do not blame families. However, it is also important to acknowledge that difficult relationships in childhood and adolescence, which can arise for all kinds of reasons, may be an important contributing factor for some people. In some cases they might be highly significant.[20] Research also confirms that people's friends and families can be very important in helping their loved ones recover, as we describe in Part 3. People whose home atmosphere is supportive, calm and tolerant tend to do better.[21]

Relationships

To improve my health I needed to reduce stress as much as possible. Stay away from stressful people, which meant I had to be firm with my father about how much I could see him.

Dolly Sen [22]

We are more likely to experience distress the more our experiences are invalidated and the more isolated we become from one another. Equally, the further we are from supportive, nurturing relationships, the more that invalidation and isolation will engender distress. People stripped of ameliorative influences such as a loving, supportive family and friends; comfortable, safe environments; and the trust, support and solidarity of others, are increasingly likely to experience diagnosable distress. In other words, the effects of trauma, social inequality and life events contingently interact with the less visible, less quantifiable effects of parenting, friendship, nurturing and caring. This is one reason why 'the same' event causes distress in some, but not others.

Midlands Psychology Group [23]

6.3 Inequality, poverty, racism and discrimination

We all deal with many stressful events in our lives. The normal and inevitable cycles of childhood, adolescence, gaining or not gaining qualifications, employment, relationships and the end of relationships, disease and death affect us all. These major life events are often stressful. In addition, ongoing stress can affect us – overwork, poor housing, financial difficulties, relationship problems and so on. And all these pressures are worse if you're poor or a member of a minority which is subject to prejudice and discrimination.[24,25]

Stress and poverty impact significantly on mental health, leading public health researchers to refer to the 'social determinants' of mental health problems. In the words of a review for the World Health Organisation: 'No group is immune to mental disorders, but the risk is higher among the poor, homeless, the unemployed, persons with low education.' Research carried out in the

Netherlands found that people who had experienced racism or other forms of discrimination were more likely to develop unusual or paranoid beliefs ('delusions').[26] Recent research in London[27] suggested that two of the three main risk factors for developing distressing psychosis were deprivation and the experience of living in dense, urban environments. The researchers suggest that 'the urban environment can modify brain function in adulthood in response to stress'. Interestingly, the third risk factor was inequality – poor people living in neighbourhoods where richer people also lived, tended to do worse than those living in neighbourhoods where most people had a similar income. This finding is similar to those of researchers Richard Wilkinson and Kate Pickett, whose book *The Spirit Level* [28] presented evidence that rates of mental health problems are higher in unequal countries – those with larger gaps in income between rich and poor, such as the UK – than in countries that are more equitable, for example Norway.

People from minority ethnic backgrounds, particularly people of African and African-Caribbean heritage living in the UK, are much more likely than white British people to be diagnosed with schizophrenia,[29] This is true both for people who have moved to the UK from other parts of the world and for those born in the UK. The reasons for this are complex. Firstly, those of us who have to live with ongoing and everyday racism are more likely to experience all kinds of mental health problems, including psychosis.[30,31,32] Secondly, many people from BME communities live in cities, and as mentioned above, rates of psychosis are higher in urban areas.[33] Thirdly, when we come into contact with services, those of us from BME backgrounds, and especially young black men, are more likely than others to receive a diagnosis of schizophrenia, even if the problems we are experiencing are much the same.[34,35] We are also more likely to be detained ('sectioned'), subjected to solitary confinement ('seclusion')[36,37] medicated against our will, and given higher doses.[38,39] This difference appears to be the result of misunderstanding, discrimination and stereotyping within services.[40,41,42] Most people assume that racism refers to people being personally racist – for example, engaging in overtly and explicitly racist verbal abuse or actively treating people differently because of their ethnicity. However, a series of government inquiries have identified that, within institutions like the police or health service, people from black and minority ethnic backgrounds can end up being treated differently even if individual members of those institutions do not individually act in this way: this is known as institutional racism (see section 13.5.1). Fourthly, as a result of this institutional racism people are also less likely to seek help early, and this can lead to a vicious circle.[43,44]

This complex pattern of discrimination and disadvantage is not only dependent on a person's skin colour: white Irish people can experience similar issues, for example, although usually not to the same degree. The different forms of prejudice can be cumulative. For instance, if you happen to be gay, black, working class, a woman and a member of a minority religious group, you may experience multiple forms of discrimination, from different sources, all with potential consequences for your mental health.

Section 7: The way we make sense of the world: the psychology of 'psychosis'

Key points

Our past experiences affect how we experience and interpret things that happen in the present. How we make sense of events is crucial in determining how they affect us.

Understanding how people make sense of their experiences is important in helping them find ways to reduce the distress associated with them.

The way that psychologists understand experiences such as paranoia and hearing voices has changed radically over the last 20 years, as has our understanding of why they can be so distressing. We have come to realise the importance not only of life events, but of the ways that people make sense of those events and also of experiences such as hearing voices.

7.1 The psychological link between life events and psychosis

The link between life events and psychosis often seems to lie in what psychologists like to call 'psychological processes' – the way we experience, interpret and react to the world and other people.

Even where there is no obvious direct link, distressing or traumatic events during a person's childhood can affect the way that the person experiences and interprets things later in life.[1] An example might be people who grow up in a school environment where they are persistently bullied. Those people might develop beliefs that they are worthless, that other people are likely to harm them, and that the world is a callous and unfeeling place. Other experiences that can lead to psychosis are threat or abuse, particularly from caregivers, or any events that lead to overwhelming emotions. Naturally, such events affect the way we subsequently experience things and see the world. Everybody interprets and reacts to new events and challenges in the light of previous experience. So people who have experienced trauma in the past can sometimes become overwhelmed or mentally 'cut off' when something happens that makes them fearful. People who have been victimised or subject to racism, hate crime or other forms or prejudice and discrimination may develop a wary and vigilant – or even paranoid – way of engaging with the world. Indeed, this may be part of the reason that 'delusions' are more common among those of us who are poor, immigrants or members of marginalised communities.[2] Particular life events seem to be associated with particular psychotic experiences. For example, Professor Richard Bentall and colleagues have found some evidence that childhood sexual abuse is more likely than other types of abuse to lead to hearing voices, whereas those brought up in institutional care are slightly more likely than others to experience paranoia.[3]

7.2 Hearing voices, inner speech and memories

Most of us at times have difficulty distinguishing what is 'real' or external from what is imagined or internal ('Did you say something?' 'Was that the doorbell?'). This tends to happen more if we are tired, stressed or upset. Most of us also experience an 'inner voice' when thinking in words, for example, when deciding what to do, struggling with a problem, or reading. Evidence that for some people voice hearing is linked with 'inner speech' comes from brain scanning experiments which show that speech areas in the brain are often active when people hear voices.[4] Other psychological experiments show that some people who hear voices can experience difficulty distinguishing between their thoughts and words spoken to them.[5] This blurring of the distinction between inner and outer speech might be part of the reason that some people hear voices more often than others. Voices are also often related to memories. For example, someone might hear the voice of someone who abused or criticised them in the past, and indeed voices can sometimes take on identities similar to real people in the person's past. Some people relate to their voices more as people or beings than as sensory experiences.[6] Sometimes voices express feelings and ideas that are not clearly memories, but express an aspect of the person's emotional life in some way. Over time, particularly when they are able to talk about their experiences in therapy and perhaps process some traumatic memories, people sometimes describe a transition from hearing them outside, to seeing them as their own thoughts or memories.

Links between life events and voices

What I would ultimately learn was that each voice was closely related to aspects of myself and that each of them carried overwhelming emotions that I'd never had an opportunity to process and resolve – memories of sexual trauma and abuse, of shame, anger, loss, and low self-worth. The voices took the place of this pain and gave words to it. And possibly one of the greatest revelations was when I realised that the most hostile, aggressive voices actually represented the parts of me that had been hurt the most profoundly – and as such, it was these voices that needed to be shown the greatest compassion and care.

Eleanor Longden: presentation at TED 2013, California [7]

7.3 How we develop beliefs and reach conclusions

As human beings we are constantly making sense of our world. Sometimes the conclusions we come to are frightening, and sometimes we're mistaken. Sometimes we see or hear things that aren't there. Sometimes our judgements are affected by our past experiences – if we've survived bullying, abuse or racism, for example, it might be difficult to trust people and we might understandably become a bit paranoid. Sometimes – for example when we've drunk alcohol or taken drugs, or sometimes even when we haven't – the way our brain is functioning can affect our judgement. But in each case, we are actively making sense of our world. Recent research into 'psychotic' experiences has found that often this sense-making or interpretation of events ('cognitive factors' in technical language) can play an important role.

Unusual beliefs ('delusions') are very similar to other beliefs or prejudices. Many 'normal' beliefs involve a resistance to change and a bias towards evidence that confirms one's initial suspicions.[8] An example might be a football supporter who sees one win as confirmation that his or her team is the best, despite a long run of lost matches. We can probably all think of friends or family members who hold on to particular beliefs despite – as we see it anyway – all the evidence.

There is a vigorous debate over what might lead to someone developing a particular 'delusional' belief, and indeed the process appears to be different for different people. Some people's beliefs relate closely to things that have happened in their lives.[9] For some they may protect self-esteem.[10] For some they are related to a particular thinking style, such as a tendency to reach conclusions quickly.[11, 12, 13] For others, they may be related to difficulties in social situations,[14, 15] or to being particularly aware of one's thoughts or of things happening around them.[16] Often the reason will be a combination of these and other things.

7.4 The relationship between emotions and psychosis

As we saw above, experiences such as hearing voices are often linked to our emotions and can sometimes have their origins in experiences that provoked overwhelming emotion. The way we make sense of things and reach conclusions is also affected by our emotions.

When we are feeling stressed, anxious, depressed or overwhelmed, the ways that we think about the world and ourselves change. We become more self-conscious, more self-critical, and more aware of risks and dangers. If we suspect that people are trying to harm us, or worry that the voices we hear can do bad things, we are likely to be more easily convinced when we are in a negative emotional state. And, of course, these links work the other way round as well. If you are hearing voices threatening to do bad things, you are quite likely to be anxious, suspicious and perhaps depressed. This close relationship with emotions means that anything that helps with emotional problems (for example, dealing with sources of stress, or perhaps psychological therapy focused on anxiety or depression) can also help with psychosis.[17] Similarly, if someone is experiencing a crisis where their experiences are overwhelming, anything that can help them feel calmer (kind, reassuring words, for example, or good food, or a peaceful place to stay) will be very useful in helping to break the vicious circle of experiences and emotions that may be going on. Often the best way to reduce the likelihood of future psychotic crises is to find ways to reduce the stress in our lives.

Emotional states and psychosis

One thing that you might hear a lot about is that anxiety is a trigger of suspicious thoughts. I have never been that good at recognising my own anxiety. Quite a high level of anxiety is pretty normal for me. So normal that I wouldn't normally do anything about it, but I now recognise that it sets the background for the expected potential threats in any situation, and so the suspicious thoughts and ideas of reference can pop right in there.

I find people as having the most potential as a source of threat and because of that I am prone to suspicious thoughts about others. So now what I do is try to address the level of anxiety I feel in these situations.

Adam [18]

The ideas were very exciting and the more I invested in them, the more I got from them. I started to enter more and more my own world and the intense excitement meant that I found it more and more difficult to sleep. I think that sleep deprivation played a key part and in a way I started to dream while I was awake. If you notice in your dreams, you're always the central figure. Whatever happens around you is related to you and that's what my life became like. Street signs became personal messages for me. A person scratching their head was a special sign that I had to decode. Newspaper articles had special meanings. Everything revolved around me just like in a dream...

My psychosis allowed me to move on emotionally. If you look at the six or seven years before I actually had a psychotic episode, I was kind of struggling, I was blocked. The psychosis allowed me to come out of myself and move on. I very nearly became a long-term mental health patient, I strongly believe that... I want to help create better mental health services that are more enabling. I want to change the way we think about human experience.

Rufus May [19]

7.5 How psychotic experiences can lead to distress and disability

The above sections have highlighted how the things that happen to us, together with the way we make sense of them, can affect the likelihood of our having 'psychotic' experiences. As we said above, not everyone finds their experiences distressing – for some people there can even be real benefits. The question therefore presents itself: why do some people find their experiences distressing and others less so? Understanding this obviously has the potential to inform how we try to help people in distress.

7.5.1 How we make sense of our experiences

Although psychologists disagree on some of the details[20, 21] there is widespread agreement that the way people make sense of their experiences is key. If people find it difficult to make sense of what has happened, or are very scared, then they are likely to be more affected. Sometimes people try to cope with their experiences in ways that are very understandable but can make things worse, for example by using drugs or alcohol, or by withdrawing from their friends and family. Recent research has confirmed that the way people make sense of and react to their experiences can be very important in determining how distressing and disabling they go on to be.[22, 23] (Of course the way we interpret and react to our experiences is itself influenced by things that have happened to us in the past, particularly in our formative years.)

To take an example: if someone is sleep deprived or feeling anxious, and then hears someone walking behind them in the street, they might fear that the person is following them or planning to harm them. This thought can in turn make them more anxious, and more likely to notice and worry about other things, for example other people in the street. If this goes on for a while, they may end up in a state of high anxiety and begin to worry that something else is going on – for example a plot to harm them. Depending on what they are personally most afraid of, and their life experiences, context and culture, they may suspect the involvement of neighbours, the CIA, spirits or perhaps aliens. They may also hear a voice criticising them or threatening to hurt them. They may then become even more worried or paranoid, and in that state they may interpret ambiguous events even more readily as a sign that someone is trying to harm them. Their fear may lead them to change the way they behave, for example stopping going out. This avoidance makes it less likely they will discover that they are not likely to be hurt. As we explained above, a psychologist might work with the person to develop a 'formulation' of what is going on and therefore what might help. The text box gives an example of how this worked for one person.

How someone arrived at a different understanding of his experiences which was less distressing and enabled him to move on in his life

This example is taken from a paper by Professor Tony Morrison and colleagues [24]

A 22-year-old man (let's call him Dan) had received a diagnosis of schizophrenia. Clinicians described him as having 'persecutory ideas, thought broadcast (believing that other people can hear your thoughts), and a delusion that he could read others' minds'. He had initially developed these experiences and beliefs after a prolonged period of heavy use of drugs and alcohol three years earlier. He rated the probability of his beliefs being true as 100 per cent.

He had a lump in his neck, which he feared was a device that could broadcast his thoughts to others and was being used to gather evidence about him. He often checked and prodded the lump, looked around for danger, and sought reassurance from family and friends. He avoided going out in order to stay safe and tried to control his thoughts in case they were being transmitted.

Professor Morrison and colleagues point out that if Dan had had slightly different worries about the lump, he would have been likely to receive a different diagnosis and might not have been seen as psychotic. For example, had he been worried that it was cancer, and was not reassured by tests, he might have been diagnosed with health anxiety (formerly called hypochondriasis). Professor Morrison and colleagues suggest that people come to be seen as psychotic if their beliefs and fears are unusual or unacceptable within their culture.

Dan also believed that he could deliberately broadcast his thoughts and that this resulted in people obeying his wishes. He thought he could hear people – usually friends or family members – thinking bad things about him including 'I'm going to kill you'. These fears were worse when he was stressed and led to him feeling angry, anxious, depressed and experiencing physical changes including flushes and palpitations. For this reason he tried to suppress these thoughts.

In collaboration with his clinical psychologist, Dan worked out what he thought was going on. He discovered that he was stuck in several vicious circles that were keeping the problem going. Experiences earlier in his life had led him to see the world in a particular way. For example, being bullied had led him to feel bad about himself and also to find it difficult to trust others. This affected the way he interpreted ambiguous situations. For example, when he found the lump he was quicker than others might have been to reach the conclusion that it was caused by others trying to harm him. The way he reacted to these beliefs – for example isolating himself and avoiding others – prevented him finding out that they weren't true.

Together, Dan and his clinical psychologist developed a 'formulation' which they wrote down in the form of a diagram. It showed how his experiences had led him to interpret events and behave in certain ways, and used arrows to represent the vicious circles that appeared to be keeping him stuck.

It looked like this (next page):

How Dan came to understand his problems

A formulation identifying vicious circles
(the arrows represent what leads to what):

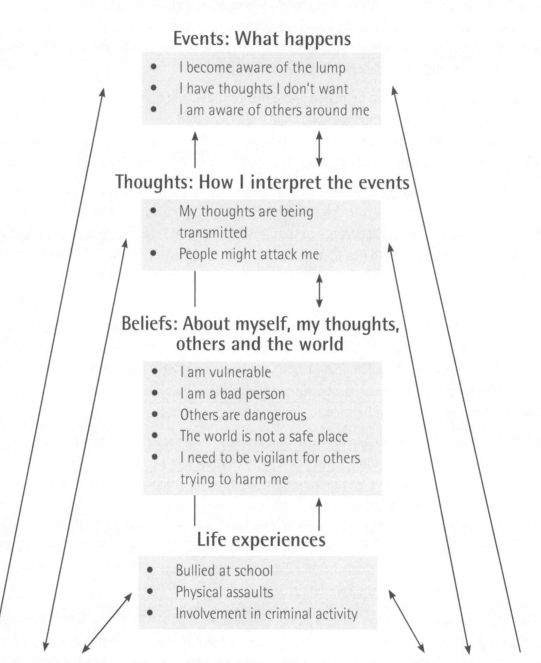

Events: What happens

- I become aware of the lump
- I have thoughts I don't want
- I am aware of others around me

Thoughts: How I interpret the events

- My thoughts are being transmitted
- People might attack me

Beliefs: About myself, my thoughts, others and the world

- I am vulnerable
- I am a bad person
- Others are dangerous
- The world is not a safe place
- I need to be vigilant for others trying to harm me

Life experiences

- Bullied at school
- Physical assaults
- Involvement in criminal activity

Responses: What I do when this happens

- Doing things that make me feel safe in the short term but prevent me checking things out
- Avoiding people
- Trying to control my thoughts. behaviours, avoidance, thought control strategies, drug use, reassurance seeking and checking, hypervigilance to threat

Feelings: How I feel

- Anxious
- Stressed
- Angry
- Emotionally aroused
- Tense

Dan and his psychologist then drew on this formulation to work out what might help. The psychologist explained that intrusive thoughts are quite common. Dan began to try to notice the thoughts as they occurred and, with help from his psychologist, worked out ways he could test them out. For example, he worked out that his belief that he could get people to do things by broadcasting his thoughts was largely based on people doing things that they were likely to do anyway, such as waving goodbye or changing gear. With the support of his psychologist he decided to experiment with trying to get people to do things which were less likely. He found that, as predicted, they rarely did these things. Together with the psychologist, Dan examined the evidence for and against his belief that he could read thoughts from other people's minds. He did this by observing closely how people behaved, and reached the conclusion that perhaps his idea that they were thinking bad things about him was in part a reflection of his own feelings of inadequacy and weakness. He was able to explore and question his negative beliefs about himself, and eventually came to feel better about himself. He also came to realise that trying to suppress his thoughts was paradoxically making them more intrusive. One thing that helped him work this out was when the psychologist suggested a 'thought experiment': trying NOT to think of a giraffe. Of course even though he rarely thought about giraffes, at that moment it was hard not to. He set himself goals and activities to ensure that he was able to go out more and re-engage with his friends. Finally he reached the point where he felt much better and was able to return to college.

7.5.2   Positive aspects of psychosis

> Men have called me mad; but the question is not yet settled, whether madness is or is not the loftiest intelligence -- whether much that is glorious – whether all that is profound -- does not spring from disease of thought -- from moods of mind... They who dream by day are cognisant of many things which escape those who dream only by night.
>
> From 'Eleonora' by Edgar Allan Poe (1850) [25]

Many people who have experienced psychosis feel that it has positive as well as negative aspects.[26, 27, 28, 29] For example, there can be a link with creativity[30] and the possible nature of this link has recently been explored in brain imaging studies.[31] 'Psychosis' sometimes appears to involve making idiosyncratic connections between events that others would see as unrelated. This is not in itself either good or bad. Sometimes making unusual connections between things is valuable and in that case it might be seen as originality, lateral thinking or creativity. In fact, people who score highly on measures of 'schizotypy' (or 'psychosis-proneness') also score highly on measures of creativity.[32] Some people who are famous for their creativity also appear to have had what might be called psychotic experiences. Examples might include Vincent Van Gogh, Stephen Fry, Joan of Arc, Winston Churchill and Ghandi. Self- help organisation *The Icarus Project* views both 'psychotic' and 'bipolar' experiences as 'a dangerous gift' and aims to help its members 'navigate the space between brilliance and madness'.[33]

There is also increasing interest in the idea that mental health crises, although painful, can sometimes lead to positive changes over the longer term – so called 'post-traumatic growth'. Some people view them as spiritual crises,[34, 35, 36] with the potential to lead to spiritual growth. This is discussed in the next section. Some people also feel that their experiences have had a role in processing and healing past trauma.[37, 38, 39]

Positive aspects of 'psychotic' and 'bipolar' experiences

My manic depression is responsible for a great deal of the positive energy and creativity in my life. For a great deal of the time I am blessed with buckets of energy – more than most people. I love to work hard. My thoughts work like liquid crystal. I can see what things mean quickly and clearly. Ideas – generally good ideas – come to me with little or no effort. I know my surfeit of energy can be irritating to others, but my brain does all the things I want it to very efficiently and I am proud of it. I feel extremely engaged with, and part of, life.

Dr Rachel Perkins OBE [40]

I … was sent for EEG tests, was told that I was hallucinating … I just felt that this really positive experience was just scrutinised and … mocked. I didn't feel offended, I just thought they were being really stupid, and disregarding this … really important thing…

Holly [41]

One with all the women

Once, within my own space,
A lighted space, warm amid the darkness,
I thought that I was Eve, the Virgin Mary,
Joan of Arc and many, many more
Of our foremothers
And I was one with all the women of history.

This was and is for me a high point,
Mystical experience, one that I am glad I had.
They knew only that I was 'disturbed'.
They did not know the glory
Of my experience
And I am one with all the women in history.

Una Parker [42]

7.5.3. Spirituality

> As people who have lived through extremes of mental and emotional distress, we are tired of being categorised and feared, worn down by being voices in the wilderness – voices that cry out for a humane and holistic understanding of who we are, that embraces physical and spiritual as well as psychological and emotional wellbeing.
>
> Vicky Nicholls [43]

There is growing interest in the idea of that 'psychotic' crises can sometimes be part of, or related to spiritual crises, and many people feel that their crises have contributed to spiritual growth.[44] A number of clinical psychologists have also explored the interface between psychosis and spirituality.[45, 46, 47] Some believe that at least some 'psychotic' episodes can be transformative crises that contain the potential for personal, including spiritual, growth.[48] Many people who believe that there is a spiritual element to their experiences find support from others with similar beliefs invaluable, for example within faith communities.[49]

People who see 'psychotic' crises as spiritual crises

For me, becoming 'mentally ill' was always a spiritual crisis, and finding a spiritual model of recovery was a question of life and death. My search began over 30 years ago, when I took time off from college studies to shut myself in my room alone to find God and the meaning of life. For a week or so, I listened to music, entertained myself with mental images, and had spiritual revelations. I experienced many unusual perceptions and bodily changes similar to ones that occur with drugs such as LSD. All of this climaxed with a vision of the oneness and interdependence of everything in the universe – the sort of thing that sounds foolish when put into words, but is profoundly true for those who experience it... The questions remain... If altered states have value, what is there to recover from?

Sally Clay [50]

I think the spiritual aspects... are never taken into account in terms of western psychiatry. I don't think they have got there yet. They understand that spirituality is important in terms of recovery but they don't take it into account in terms of diagnosis... Some of us have got too close or our ancestors are very close to us...we are being traumatized by this experience. Now you see, I talk about the slave trade and tears come. Do you understand me? So now I have this open channel... all the time I could hear people knocking and screaming, it was like I was haunted... When we went to Ghana and we went to the Castle...when I stood at the door I could feel my ancestor when she was at that door...You know this spirituality aspect... in terms of diagnosis that has never been addressed. I never disclosed it because...they just don't know how to deal with it.

Anon [51]

People who see 'psychotic' crises as spiritual crises *(continued)*

I suppose I have a predisposition towards belief and frequently go into churches or other religious places to 'pray' (meditate/relax). I believe there are powers that we cannot see and fully understand – perhaps love, perhaps electromagnetism. Like many people, I am not indifferent to questions about the meaning of life.

At the same time, the course of my own life has been shaped and, to some extent, diverted from its expected direction by a number of occasions when I have gone through profound, vivid and disturbing interior experiences which might be considered to be spiritual crises.
At these times – times of elation, exhaustion, anxiety, fear – I have lost firm contact with the reality accepted by those around me, have entered a space where other realities and other powers are more urgent and have experienced the consequences.

Once, down Hammersmith Broadway, considering myself Christ-like, I laid out all my possessions by the west door of a church in a diagrammatic Calvary and was picked up for crying out in the street. Another time, more recently, I believed myself the cause and focus of an impending collision between the earth and the setting sun and was found mute and unmoving in the shade of a garden hedge on Dollis Hill, North West London.

Inevitably, my beliefs and actions at times like these led to a confirmed diagnosis of 'psychotic mental illness' and all that follows from it. On more than one occasion, when I have been struggling to hold onto my humanity, uncertain whether I was good or evil, Christ-like or Satan, I have found myself locked up and abandoned in a cell, deprived of human contact, observed but not comforted.

What concerns me most are the spiritual difficulties facing individuals who enter the mental health service system. How do they value their experiences in crises? How do they withstand the scrutiny of science? How do they locate themselves within a society that sees them as damaged human beings?

There are a number of possible responses to 'psychotic episodes'. One is to view them as aberrations without intrinsic value. This seems to be a common approach in psychiatry and is the one I have almost always encountered there. Although it is important to define the causes of crises, the contents are not important. They are not worth understanding or are not capable of being understood – 'like the workings of a steam engine whose pistons have fallen off', as a psychiatrist once put it to me. As a result the main action that is necessary is to intervene, often in medical ways, to control the episodes and prevent them happening again.

While I do not deny the value of practical crisis prevention, I feel such an approach is destructive. It not only suggests to me that the contents of my crisis are dangerous and impenetrable, but also presses me to separate myself from them. This I cannot easily do.
Nor, I suspect, can many who experience similar crises. They remain part of us. We want to incorporate our insights into our lives, not to bind them in protective wrapping and carry them around with us as hidden baggage.

Peter Campbell [52]

Part 3: What can help

Introduction to Part 3

Part 2 showed how each person's difficulties are likely to have arisen, and be maintained by a unique combination of interacting factors. Whilst not everyone finds their experiences distressing, Part 3 describes the forms of help that are, or should be available for those who do. First of all people need the opportunity to work out what is going on – what might be causing the problem and keeping it going. We also need support from our friends, families and communities, and this is the first type of help we describe here, together with self-help. We then go on to describe how professionals can help (sometimes called 'treatment'). In this section we describe the vital practical and emotional support that mental health workers can provide, which needs to focus on helping people achieve their personal goals. Next we cover psychological or talking-based therapies. Psychologists have been very active over recent years in developing and evaluating these approaches, which have the potential to revolutionise the way that services approach psychosis. Finally, we consider the pros and cons of medication, and the different ways people use it.

Section 8: Arriving at a shared understanding of the problem

Key points

Psychologists work by collaborating with people to develop a 'formulation': a shared understanding and description of the person's main problems and what might help.

Formulations include possible causes, potential triggers, ideas about what might be keeping the problems going, and a summary of the strengths and resources that the person can draw on.

Formulations are useful in suggesting what might help.

Before deciding what might help, someone who is experiencing distressing voices or paranoid thoughts will want to work out how they understand them: why they might have started, what is keeping them going, and what makes them so distressing.

8.1 Formulation

A formulation is a way of making sense of, or understanding what is going on. Formulations often take the form of written summaries or diagrams, developed by a process of collaboration between the professional and the service user. A formulation:

1. Summarises the person's main problems.

2. Suggests how the difficulties may relate to one another. For example there may be vicious circles going on as we saw with Dan's story in section 7.5. Psychological 'models' (theories) of the processes that may be involved will be useful to draw on here.

3. Suggests what might have led the person to experience the difficulties, and why here and now.
4. Suggests what might help, including how the person might be able to draw on their own particular strengths.
5. Is always a tentative 'best guess', and open to revision and re-formulation.
6. Is developed collaboratively and agreed by both parties (the clinician and the service user).
7. Where a multi-disciplinary team is involved, the formulation informs the person's overall care plan.[1]

Formulations explore the personal meaning of the events, relationships and social circumstances of someone's life, and of their current experiences or distress. Unlike a diagnosis, formulation is based on the assumption that, however extreme, unusual or overwhelming the nature of that distress, '... at some level it all makes sense'.[2] The person experiencing the difficulty works together with the professional to develop a hypothesis, or best guess, about why voices (for example) might have appeared, in the context of the person's life experiences and the sense they have made of them. This can suggest the best way forward.[3]

In some settings the term 'formulation' is used for a description that accompanies a 'diagnosis', giving some additional details about the person. However, in the sense used here, formulations are generally alternatives to diagnosis. Recent professional guidelines suggest that this is how clinical psychologists should use them (in their clinical practice at least, although we may still need some way of categorising problems for the purposes of service planning).[4] Briefly, clinical psychologists argue that if we can provide, through psychological theory and evidence, a reasonably complete account of why someone may hear voices, hold unusual beliefs or experience paranoia, there is no need for an extra explanation such as 'they have schizophrenia as well'. Indeed, this would not really be an explanation anyway, since diagnosis in mental health is really a process of categorising rather than explaining experiences, and as we outlined above, its usefulness has been challenged even in that regard. In the words of clinical psychologist Professor Richard Bentall, 'Once these complaints (the experiences or problems that someone describes) have been explained, there is no ghostly disease remaining that also requires an explanation. Complaints are all there is.'[5] Some psychologists believe that many of what we have traditionally called 'complaints' or 'symptoms' are survival strategies which were essential at the time but which have outgrown their usefulness.[6] A formulation can help to make sense of them.

Eleanor's story

A turning point for me came when I was referred to a new psychiatrist, Pat Bracken. The very first time I met him he said to me, 'Hi Eleanor, nice to meet you. Can you tell me a bit about yourself?' So I just looked at him and said 'I'm Eleanor and I'm a schizophrenic.' And in his quiet, Irish voice he said something very powerful, 'I don't want to know what other people have told you about yourself, I want to know about you.' It was the first time that I had been given the chance to see myself as a person with a life story, not as a genetically-determined schizophrenic with aberrant brain chemicals and biological flaws and deficiencies that were beyond my power to heal. Previously I'd been told by a psychiatrist that I would have been better off with cancer as it would have been easier to cure. Pat Bracken was so much more humane than that. And he didn't talk about auditory hallucinations; he talked about hearing voices, and unusual beliefs rather than delusions, anxiety rather than paranoia. He didn't use this terrible mechanistic, clinical language; he just couched it in normal language and normal experience… I've always had a dominant voice and that has been constant throughout my experience. He has named himself and given himself an identity. He has a physical form, Machiavellian and rather grotesque. He is the archetypal horror film figure…

I began to slowly realise that yes, he is a demon, but he was a personal demon. Everyone has their private demons and his demonic aspects were the unaccepted aspects of my self-image, my shadow, so it was appropriate that he was so shadowy. He'd always been dismissed as this psychotic hallucination, but even his physical form did have meaning to it. The only way I recovered was by learning that this grotesque aspect of him is superfluous. The contempt and loathing that he expresses is actually to do with me in that it reflects how I feel about myself. He is like a very external form of my own insecurities, my own self-doubt and that is the part that is relevant and does need attending to, does need taking seriously because he is meaningful. What he says is a very powerful statement about what I am feeling about myself, and in that respect I do relate him to me by learning to deconstruct this figure and learn what is relevant and what isn't. He has a lot of relevance and a lot of personal meaning and he is capable of making very powerful statements about issues in my life that I need to deal with. This included childhood abuse, as well as adulthood experiences of injustice and adversity. It is difficult because voices are often metaphorical and you need to find the literal meaning in a figurative form of speech and seek the personal relevance in it. For instance, when he talks very violently about mutilation and death I see it as a barometer and realise that I need to take better care of myself and attend to my own needs more. It sounds like a bizarre thing to say, but he is useful in that he does provide insight into conflicts that I need to deal with.

It took a long time, but it got to the point where my demons could be cast out. While he is still around – he has never left and he is still there – he has lost his power to devastate me. I listen to him now because I understand that I'm actually listening to me. I don't catastrophise him. I see that like when my mum gets very stressed, she gets bad headaches; when I get very stressed, I hear really bad voices. I now show respect to him and he is now more likely to show me respect. Essentially, this represents taking a more compassionate, empathic and forgiving stance towards myself.

Eleanor Longden [7]

In developing a formulation, the following questions might be useful for the professional and the person concerned to consider together:[8]

1.   *What are the problems?* A shared understanding of the problems is vital and should be expressed in the person's own everyday language, e.g. 'I get very upset because people stare at me and I worry that they are thinking bad things about me.' Different people may understand their problems in very different ways depending on their background, culture or subculture,[9] beliefs and previous life experiences. It is important for professionals to bear these things in mind, to ask about them (see for example the 'cultural formulation interview'[10] developed by Dr Sushrut Jadhav), and to respect the person's framework of understanding. What does the person find most distressing? How do the problems interfere with their life or stop them doing things they would like to do?

2.   *What might have led to the problems starting?* For example, early experiences of neglect or criticism can lead us to hold deep seated views of ourselves that are very negative, e.g. 'I am worthless', 'I am a failure.' What was the personal meaning of the events and/or circumstances, and what was their impact on the person? For example, abuse may have left someone feeling ashamed or guilty; domestic violence might have convinced someone that they were worthless and trapped; poverty might have led someone to feel excluded and devalued. Some people – perhaps particularly those who see their problems in terms of an illness – might wonder about the role of some kind of genetic predisposition. All these ideas are likely to develop in the course of the conversation as the two people try to make sense of the experiences.

3.   *What triggers the problems, what sets them off?* For example 'Whenever I feel sad, the voices start. This tends to be when I'm on my own.'

4.   *What keeps the problem going?* This might be thoughts (e.g. 'people are right to judge me') things we do (e.g. 'I try to avoid going out'; 'When I go out I keep my head down and try not to look at people') and/or getting stuck in difficult patterns of interactions with others.

5.   *What strengths and resources does the person have?* What personal and social resources have protected the person and prevented the problems from escalating? Examples might include the courage to continue going out despite anxieties, or supportive relationships with friends who are not judgemental. How can these strengths be built upon and reinforced?

The text box gives an example of what the resulting formulation might look like.

An example of a formulation

Jane is 20 and has started to hear critical and hostile voices. If she has been given a diagnosis, it would most likely be psychosis or schizophrenia. Alternatively, a written formulation developed with Jane over a few weeks or months might look something like this:

You had a happy childhood until your father died when you were aged eight. As a child, you felt very responsible for your mother's happiness, and pushed your own grief away. Later your mother remarried and when your stepfather started to abuse you, you did not feel able to confide in anyone or risk the break-up of the marriage. You left home as soon as you could, and got a job in a shop. However, you found it increasingly hard to deal with your boss, whose bullying ways reminded you of your stepfather. You gave up the job, but long days at home in your flat made it hard to push your buried feelings aside any more. One day you started to hear a male voice telling you that you were dirty and evil. This seemed to express how the abuse made you feel, and it also reminded you of things that your stepfather said to you. You found day-to-day life increasingly difficult as past events caught up with you and many feelings came to the surface. Despite this you have many strengths, including intelligence, determination and self-awareness, and you recognise the need to re-visit some of the unprocessed feelings from the past. You have friends who will support you in this.

In this example the emphasis is on how the problems started and developed over time (what psychologists call a 'developmental formulation'). The example given in section 7.5 above (Dan's story) included more detail about what was keeping the problem going in the present – what psychologists call a 'maintenance formulation'.

8.2 Deciding what is likely to help

The next section describes the different forms of help that are available. For most of us, what is most important is the practical and emotional help that we receive from our friends, families and communities. We therefore deal with this first. We then describe the various forms of professional help that are available. These include the talking-based approaches (psychological therapies) which the National Institute for Health and Care Excellence (NICE) recommends should be available to everyone who experiences distressing psychosis. It is important to remember that not everyone finds it helpful to focus directly – at least in the first instance – on their experiences or unusual beliefs. They may want to focus on other aspects of their life – for example, improving their mood, or finding work – or to work on developing existing strengths. Once someone is aware of what is available, they themselves are in the best position to decide what is likely to help and it is important that they are able to exercise this choice wherever possible rather than the professionals making the decisions. They may also need to try things out to see what is most helpful.

Types of help can be divided into four broad categories, and the next sections take each of these in turn.

- Self-help, and help from friends, family and our communities (Section 9)
- Practical and emotional help from professionals (Section 10)
- Talking based approaches/psychological help (Section 11)
- Medication (Section 12).

Section 9: Self-help and help from family, friends and communities

Key points

Although professional support can be helpful, often the most important source of help and support is our network of relationships: friends, family and community.

A useful role for professionals is helping friends, family and self-help groups to support people.

There is an active 'service user and survivor' movement, which offers a community of support and a forum for campaigning.

Introduction

The community – our own existing network of relationships, and new ones that we develop – is the most important source of help for many people, although it is often overlooked in favour of a focus on 'treatments' delivered by professionals. Whatever the nature of someone's difficulties, the most important things are those we all need – supportive relationships, good housing, freedom from constant money or other worries, enjoyable and meaningful things to do, and a valued role within our community. Often it helps to concentrate less on our difficulties, and more on our strengths and potential.

The Mental Health Foundation's *Strategies for Living* project asked people with mental health problems what helps them most.[1] The findings were both ordinary and ground-breaking in that they showed clearly that it is generally not 'treatment' that helps people most, but more everyday things. Relationships with professionals and therapists were helpful, but more important were those with friends, family and other service users – people that we spend much more time with. Medication could be helpful but so were other strategies such as finding ways of obtaining peace of mind or thinking positively, religious and spiritual beliefs and lifestyles that promote health and wellbeing. What appeared to underlie the strategies that people chose or discovered was the need for:

* Acceptance
* Shared experience and shared identity
* Emotional support...'being there'
* Reason for living
* Finding meaning and purpose
* Peace of mind and relaxation
* Taking control and having choices
* Security and safety
* Pleasure.

9.1 Support from friends and family

Support from friends and family is often the most important form of help. The organisation Re-think Mental Illness[2] asked people who had used mental health services how friends and family members can best help. The most important ways appeared to be:

- Acceptance – showing love and support, valuing the person's views and opinions.
- Education – learning about what the person is experiencing and how you might be able to help.
- Mediation – offering to accompany your friend or relative to appointments, to mediate between them and mental health staff, or to act as an advocate on their behalf if needed.
- Helping the person to regain their independence after a crisis – encouraging them to go out, to join a support or self-help group, and to do things independently. Being patient – people need to move at their own pace.
- Finding a balance between independence and dependency. Both extremes can be harmful; independence can lead to isolation, while dependency can lead to people getting stuck in a 'sick role'.
- Remembering the fun things in life – going out and doing ordinary things together can make all the difference to a person's recovery.
- Family members need to take care of their own needs – if you are experiencing stress, it is difficult to help someone else.

9.1.1 How services can help friends and family to support people

Although relationships can sometimes be difficult and stressful, friends and family are also most people's main source of help and support, even for people who live alone. Sometimes they are referred to as 'carers', although there is a debate about how helpful the term is in this context.[3]

Friends and relatives are often not sure how best to help. Sometimes trying to help is frustrating and difficult, for example when a loved one is withdrawn, 'lost' in their experiences, or acts in an embarrassing or disruptive way. Often the stressful events that have led to someone experiencing a crisis are ones that also affect the whole family, so everyone is dealing with increased stress. Sometimes, even though they are trying to help, friends and family can become critical or actively hostile towards the person, or perhaps respond by trying to look after them rather as if they were a child again. While this reaction (which some researchers refer to as 'emotionally over-involved') is understandable and can sometimes be helpful in the short term, over the longer term it can be unhelpful and exhausting for everyone. Either or both of these attitudes (i.e. criticism and/or over-involvement) have been described as 'high expressed emotion' and if extreme can lead to poorer outcomes.[4] Conversely, where friends and relatives are able to maintain a calm and relaxed atmosphere at home, it can make all the difference to the person's recovery.

How family and friends can help

I couldn't have got through the experience (a psychotic episode and time in hospital) without family and friends. My brother, who was unwell himself, took me home to my parents when he saw I was getting ill. We shared a very surreal tube journey home during which I told him the people at work were witches and that I needed to be exorcised. He generously nodded and said, 'OK, Jen'. My parents took me to the local GP and then to hospital. They were there when I raced, terrified, around the hospital ward, and also when I came round some three days later and said to my mum, 'I think I've been acting a bit strangely'. She sat by my bed and hugged me. My boyfriend sat with me holding my hand while my head was spinning with ridiculous notions and ideas. After I'd come round my brother brought craft materials with him to make a card for his girlfriend. We didn't talk about where we were or what had happened, we talked about cutting up photos to make the card. I helped him a bit with the photos of sky. Well, maybe 'helped' is too generous a word! Hospital was a strange, unknown place. Having visitors helped me to keep my spirits up and believe I was going to go home soon. It must have been hard for them to come to a strange concrete building and make a visit they didn't think they'd have to make. For me it meant the world. It meant normal life flowing into a place that was not normal at all. It meant relationships and connections that helped me build resilience. I found, when I was experiencing a psychotic episode, that I sensed connections between all things, permeating us all. Afterwards, it was the connections between my loved ones that meant so much. I will forever be grateful to all my loved ones who showed me such warmth, generosity and friendship through that time, and have continued to through the times to come. If a loved one of yours has had to go into hospital, please do go and visit them. Your being there will make all the difference. Don't be scared of what to say. Say anything. Say nothing. Ask them how they are. Talk about a film you've seen recently, or your cats, or the fact that your boiler's on the blink. It doesn't matter, just sharing your solidarity at a difficult time: it breathes life into any situation, no matter how hard it seems.

Jen [5]

It is vital that services offer information and support to friends and family as well as to the person experiencing psychosis. It can be very stressful and confusing trying to help a family member who is distressed by voices or unusual beliefs, and friends and relatives need support in their own right.[6] Even if the person does not want their personal information shared with relatives, services can offer everyone general information about the problems that people can experience, what can help (give them a copy of this report, perhaps) and what is available locally.[7] All staff working in services should be trained in working with friends and families.[8]

9.1.1.1 Family meetings (sometimes called 'Family Interventions')

Many families find it helpful to have a number of meetings with a professional who is specifically trained in helping families. Clinical psychologists have been at the forefront of developing and evaluating 'family interventions', and some people find them as helpful, or sometimes even more helpful than other 'treatments' such as individual therapy or medication.[9, 10, 11] NICE recommends that everyone diagnosed with psychosis should have access to 'family interventions'[12], although unfortunately this is far from being the case.[13] The aims of the meetings might include:

- Providing an opportunity for the person to explain how they understand their experiences and how they would like the family or friends to help.
- Developing a shared understanding of what is going on and how it affects everyone involved.
- Separating out the problems from the person, and helping family members to understand that the problems are not the person's fault.
- Exploring any 'vicious circles' that may be going on. For example, a relative may feel stressed if their family member is withdrawn or appears not to be looking after themselves properly. This may lead them to be critical, and the criticism may in turn stress the person more. Their experiences may then become more intense, and the relative also more stressed.
- Improving relationships, exploring possible over-involvement and why it might be happening, and reducing any perceived criticism or hostility.
- Recognising each other's strengths.
- Working out possible solutions to problems and negotiating constructive solutions.
- Jointly developing coping strategies and ways of dealing with practical challenges.
- Negotiating roles and how friends and relatives can be supportive whilst living their own lives.

Helping families

I felt very much understood. That was very overwhelming in a way, having come from a place where we weren't understanding each other at home, to have two people who were empathic there for me and for our son Jack.

Jack's mother [14]

The family therapy has been an extremely important bond between the services of care and the family. We have grown as a family to understand the difficulties and challenges of caring for my brother who has severe psychosis. We have learned the meaning of the psychosis – it has been extremely educational... The most important part of the family therapy has been the reflection and listening without judgement... That is the wonderful thing about the family therapy – it embraces the difference without judgement.

Fari

Sometimes it can be helpful for groups other than families to have such meetings. For example, someone might want to have similar conversations with friends, flatmates or close work colleagues. For the small number of people who are very disabled by their experiences and live in supported accommodation, it can be helpful to have similar meetings with the staff who provide the support, perhaps facilitated by someone from the local mental health team.

In some mental health services, family meetings are based on the traditional idea that the 'identified patient' has an illness which other family members need to understand and make allowances for. However, in others the starting point for meetings is that different people are likely to have different beliefs about the nature and causes of the problem and what might help. The aim of meetings is to arrive at an understanding of the problem that is acceptable to all involved, and to use that understanding to plan a possible way forward.[15] The most non-directive of such approaches, 'Open Dialogue',[16] originates from Finland[17] but is becoming increasingly popular in the UK. Where services use this approach, as soon as someone is referred workers ask for their permission to arrange regular meetings. Meetings could include mental health staff, the person themselves and all those around them including family members, employer, neighbours and friends. The meetings offer a chance for all those involved to listen to each other and take seriously each other's understanding of what is going on. All decisions are made at these meetings. It is reported that within such services, fewer than a third of people are prescribed neuroleptic medication. Although randomised controlled trials (sometimes called the 'Gold Standard' for research) have not yet been undertaken, recovery rates appear to be high, both in terms of reduced 'symptoms' and use of services, and in terms of 'social' recovery, for example being able to return to work.[18]

9.2 Self-help and mutual support

> Self help can save you, self help can soothe
> By offering a safe place to gently remove
> Those thoughts that go unsaid so often for years
> Locked up in frustration anger and fear
> Who will accept me if they know I'm flawed?
> Will all conversation leave me ignored?
> So often we need to relate to a friend
> Who will listen and empathise
> And help us to mend.
>
> Jean Cave [19]

There are also many ways that people who are experiencing paranoia or distressing voices can help themselves and each other. Feeling isolated can be a major source of stress to people who are struggling with distressing experiences. Meeting other people with similar experiences in self-help groups and other settings can be key to feeling less alone, and people are able to learn from each other about what can help. There are groups for people who share particular experiences, for example hearing voices or self-harm. Black users of mental health services have often formed self-help groups because services were not culturally appropriate - or sufficiently available - and because, given the existence of racism in society and in institutions like mental health services, they felt there was a need to create a safe space for people from BME backgrounds.[20,21] There are also women-only and LGBT-only groups, for example. Collective approaches like this can also be helpful in building a sense of solidarity between members.

> Being accepted in my full humanity, with my differences, has also been vital and something I have been more likely to find among fellow survivors than within services.
>
> Peter Campbell [22]

Some self-help groups run independently and others are facilitated or co-facilitated by mental health workers. Often workers act in a facilitative role, offering support in the background, with the aim of withdrawing once group members are able to run the group.[23]

Sometimes individuals make their own self-help materials available for the benefit of others, sharing their experience and helpful strategies they have used. Examples can be found in the 'resources' section at the end of this report.

9.2.1 The Hearing Voices Network

The Hearing Voices Network (HVN)[24] is a network of self-help groups for 'people who hear voices, see visions or have unusual perceptions'. It originated from the work of Dutch psychiatrist, Marius Romme, and his colleague Sandra Escher. The HVN is explicitly based on the idea that different people have different ideas about the nature and causes of their experiences. There are over 180 groups across the UK which meet regularly and give people the opportunity to talk freely and to support one another. HVN is also active internationally.[25]

> I'd been living all these years in a strange isolated bubble, thinking I was unique, and then I realised there were all these other people just like me.
>
> Ruth, a member of a Hearing Voices Network group [26]
>
> I began attending a self help hearing voices group where I met others who could hear voices too. Here we shared with each other our experiences and exchanged coping techniques.
> We had bizarre conversations that, in any NHS setting might lead to a mass sectioning!
> I was introduced to others who accepted my experiences as part of who I am and not part of a medical illness ... I didn't believe I was a psychiatric patient with a lifelong brain disease any more, but an overcomer of childhood sexual abuse, an activist for change in the current system that is based on an outdated medical model.
>
> Sally Edwards

9.2.2 Complementary approaches

There have been few formal trials of complementary therapies such as massage, yoga and exercise. However, many people find that they help to reduce the high levels of stress and arousal which often play a role in mental health crises.

> To improve my health I needed to learn and practice relaxation techniques. Only a few months of yoga and meditation and everyone, I mean everyone, noticed the difference.
>
> Dolly Sen [27]

9.2.3 Peer Support

Peer support is a term used to describe mutual support between people who use mental health services.[28]

There are three types of peer support:[29]

* Informal, naturally occurring peer support (for example, between two people who are both inpatients on the same ward)
* Participation in service user run (peer-run) groups or programmes
* Service users as paid providers of services – formal peer support.

There is considerable evidence that the first type of support is common[30] and very valuable in hospitals and other mental health services.[31] The second type (self-help groups) was described above. The third type, i.e. the employment of service users as peer support workers in mainstream mental health services, is becoming increasingly common within UK mental health services and NICE recommends that services consider it.[32] Peer support workers help people by sharing their experience, providing an empathic and reciprocal relationship, and giving encouragement and hope. Research suggests that the person receiving support, the person giving it and wider services can all benefit.[33, 34, 35, 36]

Peer support

We recommend that organisations should consider a radical transformation of the workforce, aiming for perhaps 50 per cent of care delivery by appropriately trained and supported 'peer professionals'.

Centre for Mental Health[37]

I have met with mental distress throughout my life and only saw my experiences as painful or something to be ashamed of. I often found myself sitting opposite professionals who, despite their endless compassion, could not understand what was happening inside my head and all the ways it was affecting my life... The best thing about this job is not having to hide a single scrap of myself... On a personal level, this job has done more for me than any counselling session or doctor or pill ever could. The things that I've come through are being used in a constructive way. I've made peace with them and learned from them and for the first time in a long time I know in myself that I wouldn't change a second.

Emma Watson, peer support worker[38]

9.2.4 Community development approaches

Community development involves members of communities working together to develop collective solutions to common problems.[39,40,41] Community Development Workers – people skilled in facilitating collective approaches – are often key. This is a relatively recent development in mental health,[42] but a good example is the *Sharing Voices*[43] project in Bradford which brings together people from different faiths, cultures and backgrounds. The project website (www.sharingvoices.net) states that 'mental health experiences often arise from issues around: poverty, racism, unemployment, loneliness, family conflicts, relationship difficulties and cannot be merely understood through biological terms alone. So listening to people's own explanation and helping them find their solutions to problems is a key part of our work.' The project has a strong commitment to mutual aid and a number of self-help/mutual aid groups have been set up by people with first-hand experience of distress.

9.2.5 Recovery colleges: an educational approach to offering help

Recovery colleges are a new development. In contrast to the traditional approach where clinicians offer treatments, recovery colleges offer an educational approach. The aim is to help people improve their wellbeing, take control of their recovery and achieve their hopes and aspirations. Courses are designed and delivered by professionals working in partnership with people whose expertise is derived from lived experience. They are open to people who use services, their relatives and friends, and also to staff.[44, 45]

Differences between traditional services and recovery colleges	
Traditional therapeutic model	**Recovery educational approach**
People seen as patients	People seen as students
Focuses on problems and symptoms	Focuses on people's strengths, talents and resources
Prescription – nature of therapy is chosen or prescribed then offered by the expert: 'This is the treatment you need'	Choice – students choose what courses might help them, become experts in their own care: 'Which of these courses interest you?'
Professional assessment and referral	Registration/enrolment and co-production of personal learning plans
Involves an expert (therapist) and non-expert (patient) power imbalance	Involves peer trainers and traditionally qualified staff who coach or tutor students to find their own recovery path
Discharge and review	Certificate of completion and graduation

Recovery college courses are proving popular and the early evidence is that they can be an effective way of supporting people's wellbeing and recovery.[46, 47, 48, 49]

> This is the best thing to happen in mental health. It puts a person's recovery back in the service user's control.
>
> Diana Byrne, Senior Peer Trainer at Hastings and Rother Recovery College [50]

9.2.6 The service user/survivor movement

Increasingly, people are describing and reflecting on their experiences as part of a growing literature written from what could be broadly called a service user and survivor perspective.[51] Within this body of work, some major themes appear to be:

- Different views about the nature and meaning of experiences
- Seeing benefits as well as challenges in 'psychotic' experiences
- Links between 'madness', creativity and spirituality
- Feeling dehumanised by some aspects of mental health services.

Independent service user and survivor groups have flourished in recent times and are often at the forefront of introducing innovative approaches, either providing services independently or contributing to mainstream mental health services. 2007 saw the establishment of the National Survivor User Network (NSUN),[52] an independent service user-led charity that connects people with experience of mental health issues to give them a stronger voice in shaping policy and services.

Section 10: Practical and emotional help from professionals

Key points

Skilled professional help can make a big difference, but workers need to be open to different ways of understanding experiences.

Getting help early can make a big difference.

Emotional support and help with practical issues such as work and employment, benefits, housing and relationships is often as important as help targeted directly at 'symptoms'.

We urgently need more crisis facilities, particularly ones based on the psychological approach outlined in this report rather than on one that sees crises primarily as relapses of an illness.

If services adopted the approach described here, there would be less need for compulsion under mental health legislation. The British Psychological Society has argued that the decision to detain someone should be based on their ability to make the relevant decisions ('capacity') rather than on whether they have a psychiatric diagnosis.

Introduction: what are services for?

This section is about the practical and emotional help and support which is often the most important thing that services provide. Traditionally, mental health services have focused on reducing 'symptoms' such as voices or paranoid thoughts. However, as we explained above, not everyone finds their experiences distressing, and not everyone understands them as symptoms.

It is vital that mental health workers are open to different ways of understanding experiences, and do not insist that people see their difficulties in terms of an illness. This simple change will have a profound and transformative effect on our mental health services.

In recent years the focus has moved to reducing distress and helping people to live the kind of life that they want, whether or not the experiences continue. This has sometimes been termed a 'recovery' approach. This approach has been the subject of some controversy because some people feel that the term recovery unhelpfully implies that there is an 'illness' to recover from. There have also been instances where it has been used as an excuse for withdrawing support from people with ongoing needs. The idea of 'wellbeing' has been suggested as an alternative.[1] However, the 'recovery' approach has driven positive change within many mental health services.[2,3] The emphasis is on each person finding their own way to a life that is meaningful and satisfying for them, drawing on personal strengths and on support from people within and outside the mental health system.[4] This last point is important: 'recovery' does *not* mean that people should be able to do without help.[5] Many people experience ongoing, disabling problems and it is vital that the idea is not used as an excuse to cut services or withdraw support.[6,7] Services need to support people in whatever way they personally find most helpful. Sometimes this is referred to as 'services on tap, not on top'.[8]

Adopting a recovery or wellbeing approach represents a major change in the culture and organisation of services, since different people may have very different goals. In the UK, the Centre for Mental Health has led the way in championing such an approach[9, 10] and the *Implementing Recovery – Organisational Change* (ImROC) programme[11] has supported mental health trusts to change their structures and practice.

Tools are available to help people take control of their own recovery and wellbeing, such as WRAP (Wellness Recovery Action Plan).[12] Such tools provide a framework to help people to identify their strengths and sources of support, to plan their time in a way that helps them to stay well, to think about what the warning signs might be of a mental health crisis and how to keep safe, and to write an 'advance directive' about what they want to happen if they are admitted to hospital.

10.1 Making sure basic needs are met

People who are coping with overwhelming experiences may need help with looking after their basic needs such as housing, money and good food.[13] Help with practical issues is often as, or even more important than traditional 'treatments' such as therapy or medication. Services need to be flexible enough to offer each individual what he or she finds most helpful at that particular point. Clinical psychologist Professor Daniel Freeman has highlighted the important role that lack of sleep, or poor sleep can play in mental health crises, and has suggested ways that services can help people to sleep better.[14, 15] Crises can often come about as a result of a vicious circle: experiences become overwhelming partly because the person needs water, food and sleep, but in their distressed, confused or over-excited state they are not able to deal with these needs themselves. Crisis services such as wards need to attend to these needs first.

> Interestingly it's often the basics which are missed in mental health patients. I worked out with a friend once that he had ended up sectioned many times on account of being incoherent because of lack of food and fluids, but this hadn't been checked. I saw it with own eyes, him looking 'sectionable', feeding/hydrating him and watching him return to sentences.
>
> Anon

10.2 Emotional support

It is hard to overemphasise the importance of care, kindness, listening and emotional support in times of distress, and this is often the most important thing that workers can offer. Research on psychiatric wards[16] found that what people valued most was 'human contact with staff'. The researchers concluded that 'even the briefest of human communication had a disproportionately powerful and positive effect if it was based on an empathetic approach'.

How services and workers helped

I was an active participant in my own recovery, just as I had been active in my self- destruction. But it was my social worker Bernadette who enabled me to engage in the process, who made my recovery possible.

How did she do it? From the first, Bernadette managed to convey that she wanted to work with me. This is not a desire that can be faked; she conveyed it because she felt it. I remember bumping into her in the street very shortly after we started working together. 'How nice to see you,' she said, and it was clear to me that she meant it. The mere fact that I remember such a simple comment all these years later suggests just how potent sincerity can be.

But it wasn't just a question of what she said. Her actions reinforced her words over and over again. She never once missed an appointment... In our very first meeting, she asked me what sort of contact I'd like from her. I was, I remember, reluctant to say, unwilling, after the day hospital, to find myself turned away again, but Bernadette persisted. 'Well, I suppose, ideally, I'd like to see you every week,' I ventured. I waited for the world to end. 'That's fine,' Bernadette said.

Bernadette's commitment, her refusal to budge, her utter reliability, showing up week after week wherever I was, in hospital or out of it, her consummate patience, the sheer amount of time she was willing to offer – all these were critical in building the trust we needed to work together.

My relationship with Bernadette has been through many different phases over the years. One of the great benefits of social work is its flexibility. Early on, I needed more practical help; later, as I returned to work, she offered me a great deal of support in making the transition. Crucially, Bernadette recognised that the time someone begins to walk unaided is not the time to throw away the crutches.

Clare Allan [17]

To improve my health I needed good housing and social support. When I finally got a good place to live and had my benefits sorted out, and help with my Dad, the relief from stress was palpable. I noticed this in others who've had mental health problems and finally improved their housing or home situation... I can positively guarantee anyone who has been discharged from hospital and put in a shitty little bedsit with little human contact *will* relapse.

Dolly Sen [18]

I needed someone who would just be there – solid, non-judging, not trying to force me to do this or that, just being with me and helping me to make sense of some very frightening, but also very beautiful and visionary experiences.

Anonymous [19]

In hospital ... I was listened to seriously and attentively; my requests ... were all complied with quickly and treated with respect. Doctors did not look straight over or through me, they treated me like a substantial human being and were very sympathetic, especially concerning the terrible feelings of humiliation I had about my delusions. Nurses did not generally adopt a controlling, domineering attitude but were usually sensitive, responsive and human. Even ward domestics played a significant role in my recovery.

Peter Chadwick [20]

10.3 Work and employment

Work and/or education are often particularly important. People who are under-occupied are much more likely than others to experience recurring problems, and our sense of identity is also often bound up with the voluntary or paid work that we do. Helping people to find and keep good employment, education or other roles that they find meaningful should therefore be a core task for mental health workers.[21]

Most people who have experienced psychosis want to work, but they are one of the most under-employed groups in the UK: approximately 90 per cent of those in contact with specialist mental health services are unemployed.[22] This is very significant because there is evidence that for many people, finding or getting back to meaningful work or other valued activity can have a greater positive impact than any 'treatment'.[23] People sometimes need help to get into work and it is vital that services provide support with this.[24] NICE recommends that services should offer people tailored help with finding and keeping good employment. The most effective approach appears to be 'Individual Placement and Support'[25] where the service first helps someone find suitable work as quickly as possible, and then supports them to keep it.[26, 27, 28] This approach can be successful even for people who are still struggling with on-going and sometimes disabling experiences. If the person is not able to do paid work, then voluntary work or other meaningful activity such as education can also be very important. Again, everyone is different and it is very important that people are not pressured to return to work.

Meaningful work after a breakdown

I applied for the position of retained firefighter with the Fire & Rescue Service. I realised my diagnosis, medication and past sections would be big hurdles to overcome but following many medicals over a period of about 18 months I was eventually accepted and spent eight wonderful years serving the local community. It would have been easy to say to myself 'what's the point of applying; they'll never take someone like me', but I was aware of falling into the trap of self-stigmatising and eventually my persistence paid off. I wasn't treated any differently because of my condition and although my colleagues knew about my health problems, it was never an issue when we worked together.

James Wooldridge [29]

One of the major considerations for people who have experienced mental health problems is whether or not to inform existing or potential employers. In some cases people have good reason to fear unfair discrimination as many cases of this have been documented, despite legislation outlawing discrimination on grounds of disability and requiring employers to make 'reasonable adjustments'.[30, 31] There is an obligation to respond truthfully to direct questions from potential employers concerning any existing conditions prior to accepting a post. Where this information is not specifically requested by employers then employees are not legally required to volunteer it.[32]

10.4 Help with organisation and motivation

The majority of people who hear distressing voices or hold beliefs that others consider 'delusional' nevertheless function well in their lives. However, some people experience ongoing problems such as difficulties organising their thoughts and motivating themselves. Sometimes people can become isolated or find it hard to look after themselves properly. In traditional clinical language, such difficulties have sometimes been referred to as 'negative symptoms'. Sometimes they can be reactions to, or ways of coping with voices or paranoia. Sometimes they are related to prescribed or other drugs.[33] They can also be related to the person's situation, for example living in an unstimulating environment where there are limited opportunities to engage in meaningful activity or where people have been given the message that their problems are likely to be permanent and disabling.[34]

It is important for workers to focus on people's strengths rather than on problems. For example, one study found that nearly half of people with a mental health diagnosis who were successful in employment had previously been told by a clinician that they would never work again, a so-called 'prognosis of doom'.[35] Naturally, when people are given such a hopeless message they are likely to feel more apathetic and withdrawn, and find it harder to motivate themselves. This can create a vicious circle. It is important for all concerned to remember that most people who experience voices or have 'delusional' beliefs go on to lead successful lives.

There are a number of strategies that can be helpful. For example, 'behavioural activation' focuses on people's own interests and goals. Workers help the person to identify and plan how to reach these, and to deal with pitfalls on the way. Psychological approaches such as cognitive behaviour therapy can sometimes help by addressing worries about the new work or other activity (see below). An approach called 'cognitive remediation' (see section 11) can help people to increase their problem solving, memory and planning skills and work towards things they really want or need to do.[36]

Some people who experience continued distress or confusion may need ongoing support in order to live the kinds of lives they want to lead. Just as people with physical disabilities require environmental adaptation and prosthetic aids, so too people who are disabled by persistent distressing experiences or beliefs may require ongoing aids. For example, some people may need reminding about things or help with planning; others may need practical help with household tasks, with sorting out benefits or emotional support.

10.5 Getting help early

'Early intervention' aims to prevent or reduce the severity of problems before they are fully developed and is recommended by NICE.[37] Many areas now have specialist services which offer help to young people who are experiencing problems for the first time. The Schizophrenia Commission[38] found that these services are popular and recommended that they should be extended. Many offer practical or psychological help in the first instance, rather than rather neuroleptic medication with its attendant risks.[39, 40]

A good experience of an early intervention service

My care coordinator helped me evaluate the things I was doing in life that were more unhelpful than helpful and I started making small changes for the better. Looking at my symptoms closely helped me to identify when things were getting worse - or better; important for being able to ask for help. For me, I felt medication was a good route to try in tandem with talking therapies, but everybody finds different things useful.

Slowly the fog started lifting and I began to feel more like me again. I was able to make good use of CBT [cognitive behavioural therapy] sessions with my care coordinator and sessions with the team psychologist. This helped me understand the way I was feeling when I developed psychosis and look at new ways of coping in future situations.

With the continued support of EIP [the Early Intervention in Psychosis Service] across three years I feel like 'me' again; I have recently been discharged from the service and am no longer on any medication. I am very ambitious in my career, working full time for the last 2.5 years and am enjoying being a first-time mum to my 10-month-old baby!

Anonymous[41]

10.6 Help at times of crisis

Many people need help only occasionally when their problems become so severe that they, or their family and friends, feel unable to cope. When it is friends or relatives who feel that help is needed, workers need to bear in mind that those making this suggestion may have been coping for some time, and try to understand why help is being sought now. What do the friends/relatives and the potential service user actually feel would be helpful at this point? Is it possible to negotiate a 'contract' with commonly agreed goals? There is a need for creative responses to such situations, which build on what service users themselves say is helpful.[42] Sometimes the only help available is admission to an acute psychiatric ward, and sometimes not even that: ward closures have led to a situation where very distressed people sometimes have to wait for many hours in Accident and Emergency departments or sometimes even police cells.[43, 44] Whilst many people are greatly helped by a period of time in hospital, this is not the case for everyone. Sometimes acute wards operate on a simplistic 'illness model' where staff see their main role as administering medication and keeping the person safe until the drugs 'work'. People sometimes have little opportunity to talk about the reason for their admission and can be left feeling powerless and confused. Many people find acute psychiatric wards frightening and unhelpful.[45] Recent initiatives have attempted to improve things, for example the 'Star Wards'[46] project which provides ward staff with *ideas and inspiration, not standards and compulsion'*.

Help at times of crisis

What helps people hold steady in crisis and during periods of severe distress? Presumably all the people who are not in the mental health system have found a way of doing this – probably through the meaning they attach to the experience. Practical things are very important to help you keep steady and to ground yourself again as a person and in the social world. You need workers that you can trust to accompany you through the experience and who you can check things out with. So relationships are key.

Laura Lea, contributor

We should not, as a society, be leaving people with urgent mental health needs isolated, frightened and unsupported in impersonal hospital settings. We should not be traumatising those who use these services to such an extent that they would do anything not to return. Our services should not be giving people a sense of abandonment.

MIND, from *Listening to Experience* [47]

It became clear that it is not procedural approaches (such as diagnosis or care plan) which set the tone of an admission, but human contact with staff. Even the briefest of human communication had a disproportionately powerful and positive effect if it was based on an empathetic approach. We found this even when patients felt they were suffering delusions or were closed down and uncommunicative.

Neil Springham and Ami Woods, researchers on acute mental health wards [48]

A range of alternatives to acute psychiatric wards have been developed.[49] These include crisis resolution/home treatment teams, non-hospital crisis houses such as crisis houses,[50, 51] 'recovery houses'[52] and a host family scheme in Hertfordshire.[53] There are also examples of crisis services run by service users and ex-users, for example the Wokingham Crisis House[54] or the Leeds Survivor Led Crisis Service.[55] Crisis houses are very popular with those who use them.[56] There are still very few, however, and more are urgently needed.

Workers should help every service user who wants it to draw up an 'advance directive' stating what he or she wants to happen should a crisis occur in which he or she is considered temporarily unable to exercise appropriate judgement. Professionals who work in crisis services should routinely inquire about these.

All service users should also have access to independent advocacy.[58, 59]

10.7 Keeping safe

10.7.1 Self neglect, self harm and suicide
When people are in a state of distress and confusion they can sometimes need help to maintain an adequate diet, or look after their home. Someone who is confused is also likely to be at risk of exploitation and abuse from other people.

Some people in acute distress harm or even try to kill themselves. There is a debate within services about the best way to respond. Traditionally both self-harm and suicide attempts have been seen

Crisis houses

Difficult as my summer was, it could have been worse. I could have spent it sweating on a plastic mattress in NHS pyjamas, queuing up for meds three times a day, listening to the screams of my fellow patients being held down and forcibly injected. I undoubtedly would have done, were it not for the fact that I happen to live in the catchment area for one of the only two women's crisis centres in the country.

When Drayton Park opened in 1995, it was truly innovative: a residential service, designed and run exclusively for women, and aiming to offer an alternative to acute psychiatric admission. When I first went there, a year or so later, I remember my amazement, bordering on glee, at the huge saggy sofas, the home-cooked food, my room (my own room, ensuite, with a key!) and the fact that the staff appeared to want to talk to me.

Chatting with the other women, comparing our past experience, you could feel the disbelief in the air, that glazed look people's eyes take on as they sense the stocks of their own self-worth start to rise. We thought we were in at the start of a whole new movement, a revolution, that Drayton Parks would be springing up right across the country. The fact that, 10 years later, there's only one other comparable service – Foxley Lane, part of the Maudsley Hospital and, like Drayton Park, also in London – is disappointing to say the least. To my mind, it's disgraceful.

Clare Allan, in *The Guardian*[57]

as 'symptoms' and services have used coercive measures to prevent them. Most of us agree that services need to protect people from taking their own lives when they are confused and not in their normal frame of mind. However, in most other circumstances there is acceptance of the need for 'positive risk taking' – people who use services have a right to take risks, make their own choices and learn from mistakes just like anyone else. Indeed taking away people's liberty and right to make their own choices risks making them feel even more hopeless.

10.7.2 Risk to other people

As we stated above, the idea that people who experience psychosis are likely to be violent is a myth. Nevertheless, there have been instances of people attacking others, usually those with whom they have most contact, including family members and mental health staff. Sometimes people are detained for long periods because of concerns about possible risk or dangerousness. It has sometimes been assumed that violence is directly linked to the person's experiences, for example if voices tell someone to do something ('command hallucinations', in medical language). However, such instances actually seem to be quite rare.[60] Much more commonly, people who are violent are responding to the same things that might lead to violence in other settings, particularly when people are feeling powerless. For example, the majority of violent incidents on acute mental health wards happen after staff limit someone's freedom in some way, for example by denying a request, placing a restriction on them, or insisting they take medication.[61] Staff should be trained in different ways to negotiate during disputes and resolve conflicts. This should include role playing having one's freedom restricted and learning how to empathise with people when they are overwhelmed with fearful or angry feelings. Services should also offer help to families in this regard.

10.7.3 Risk of harm from services

Whilst many people have good experiences of services and professionals, all treatments bring with them the risk of doing harm as well as good. The negative effects of psychiatric drugs and other aspects of mental health services, for example the over-use of restraint in hospitals particularly with certain people such as black men and young men generally, are well documented.[62,63,64] These problems are often under-recognised and understated by professionals, perhaps because they see it as their role to persuade people to engage with services. However, mental health services are unique in that people can be compelled to use them under mental health legislation. This means that those of us who work in services have an ethical responsibility to do all we can to keep people safe from the harm that services can do.

Some of the harm that services sometimes do is related to the unrealistic expectations that we have of them as a society. This leads to a 'risk-averse' culture where workers themselves fear being blamed or criticised if something goes wrong. Together with the false assumption sometimes made that persuading people to take medication is an effective way of keeping them and others safe, this can have quite negative consequences. For example, in some services professionals who fear being criticised if anything goes wrong become over-focused on insisting that people take medication.[66]

As we outline in Section 12, there is large individual variation in response to medication. A more sophisticated approach is badly needed.

10.7.4 Compulsion: using mental health legislation

Current legislation allows for people to be kept in hospital and even administered medication against their will if they are judged to be 'mentally disordered' and to pose a risk to themselves or others. We need to remember how serious a decision this is, and how distressing it can be. The numbers of people subject to compulsion have been rising year-on-year and we view this with grave concern.[67] The number of compulsory admissions is now double what it was in the 1980s[68] and in many hospitals the majority of people are being held against their will. Although it was hoped that the controversial introduction of 'community treatment orders' would reduce this number, they have been largely ineffective in preventing admissions.[69]

As we noted above, people from disadvantaged backgrounds, and particularly from black and minority ethnic communities are more likely than others to experience compulsion, both in terms of detention and forced medication. Young men of African or African Caribbean heritage are at greatest risk.[70,71,72] Services need to be aware of this tendency and take active steps to ensure that everyone is treated fairly.

There is an argument that by keeping people against their will in wards which are often unpleasant and sometimes frightening, and where often the only help on offer is medication with distressing side effects, we are failing to uphold the basic ethical principle of 'reciprocity', namely that 'where society imposes an obligation on an individual to comply with a programme of treatment or care, it should impose a parallel obligation on the health and social care authorities to provide safe and appropriate services, including on-going care following discharge from compulsion'.[73]

The British Psychological Society has argued that decisions should be explicitly based on someone's ability to make the relevant decisions ('capacity') rather than on whether he or she has a psychiatric diagnosis.[74] The law in Scotland makes this clear but this is not yet the case in England or Wales. Many admissions involve compulsory administration of medication, sometimes by force. There is a debate about whether such measures are ever justified.[75,76,77,78,79]

I would be taken by five or six nurses and pinned down and given medication. They injected it in my backside. It was quite humiliating and felt very degrading. My trousers were taken down and, I was given a needle into my buttock. It was often a very powerful medication that would leave me extremely sedated for several days...

But it didn't help me understand my confusion. It drove me away from wanting to work in partnership with the people who were supposed to be trying to help me. One time I managed to escape, and this is one of my reasons why I think compulsion is dangerous, is that it drove me to escape the hospital at a time when I was quite vulnerable. I didn't have the patience to wait for the trains so I just started walking down the track and the train came up behind me. I heard the hooter and I froze and it just stopped in front of me, just beside me, and I got onto the train. I was preoccupied with religious ideas at the time and I said: 'Do you believe in Jesus?' The train driver said, 'I don't know about him but it's a good job Harry saw you!'

Rufus May [80]

'The 'big, bad black man syndrome'... you're more likely to be heavily medicated or physically restrained. You expect it'.

Anon [81]

To have strange experiences or ones that others do not understand and which are acted upon, immediately make others frightened. When people are frightened they want 'something to be done'. If they are frightened but 'sane' by common consent in relation to agents of the State (such as the police, social workers and psychiatrists) then they will usually successfully find ways of reducing their anxiety by getting something done. Once a person then becomes a psychotic patient in the system, anxiety there will ensure that professionals also take action. They will medicate rather than wait and see, and if in doubt they will use legal powers or threaten to use them. This is why it is hard to find a non-medicated patient and why the Mental Health Act or its threat is used to control an unpredictable situation.

But this is the twist in the tail... if we are to move to a consensual, user-centred and voluntaristic ethos, where people are given genuine choices (the rhetoric of mental health Trusts not just this report) then there is a crucial consequence of knee-jerk routines of medication plus legal control. It will alienate patients and traumatise them when coerced, and thereby defeat the good intentions implied in the rhetoric. The power of the 'sane' over the 'insane' must be used very judiciously if that rhetoric is to start to become a reality.

Professor David Pilgrim, Contributor

Section 11: Talking – psychological help

Key points

Psychological therapies – talking treatments – are helpful for many people.

The National Institute for Health and Care Excellence (NICE) has reviewed the evidence and recommends that everyone with a diagnosis of schizophrenia should be offered talking therapy. However, most are currently unable to access it.

The most researched therapy is cognitive behaviour therapy (CBT). Trials have found that on average, people gain as much benefit from CBT as from medication.

'Family interventions' have also been extensively researched and many people find family meetings very helpful.

Talking therapy is very popular: demand vastly outstrips supply in the NHS.

There is an urgent need for further investment in psychological approaches to ensure that all services come up to the standard of the best, and so that people can be offered choice.

Different approaches suit different people. Not everyone finds formal psychological therapy helpful and some find it positively unhelpful. We need to respect people's choices.

All staff need to be trained in the principles of a psychological approach as outlined in this report so that it can inform not only formal therapy but also the whole culture of services and every conversation that happens within them.

Introduction

It is vital for people to be able to talk and think about their experiences in a calm, supportive and non-judgemental atmosphere. This underpins all forms of helping and should be the first thing that any worker or service offers. Providing this opportunity is often the most important thing that any mental health worker can do.

Talking therapy, also called psychological therapy, is essentially a more formalised opportunity for people to talk and think about their experiences. It helps people to make sense of their experiences, work out what they mean for them and find out what helps.

The idea that it is possible to understand 'psychotic' experiences psychologically – in other words, in the same way that we understand other human experiences – is transforming mental health services. Some of the contributors to this report have been at the forefront of this development. One important practical consequence has been that psychological therapies are now more widely available, although there is a long way to go before they are available to everyone.[1] In particular, there is evidence that people from BME and other socially disadvantaged backgrounds are much less likely than others to be offered psychological therapy. Culturally informed services, able to draw on a range of understandings of distress are also unavailable in many areas.[2,3]

All psychological therapy depends on a trusting, collaborative working relationship between therapist and client. In some cases this is probably the most important 'ingredient',[4] and it is vital that people are able to find a therapist with whom they feel comfortable. Different approaches also suit different people, depending on their preferences and on what appears to be keeping the problem going – the 'formulation' referred to above.

Talking therapy may be offered individually, in groups or to families. In this latter case it is often called 'family intervention': this was described in Section 9 above. Whilst psychological therapy has traditionally been offered in conjunction with medication, recent research suggests that it could perhaps be helpful as an alternative for some people.[5,6,7,8]

It is crucial that therapists work towards the person's own goals rather than making assumptions about what is important. For example, reducing 'symptoms' such as voices may not be the person's main goal. Clinical psychologist Professor Paul Chadwick describes the need for 'radical collaboration'.[9] Based upon the person-centred approach of Carl Rogers[10] 'radical collaboration' is based on the following assumptions:

Assumptions underlying 'radical collaboration' in psychological therapy

1. The core of people is essentially positive. Given certain therapeutic conditions (e.g. active listening and exploration of new possibilities within a transparent process) clients experiencing psychosis can move towards emotional wellbeing and acceptance.
2. 'Psychotic' experience is continuous with ordinary experience and part of the human condition - therefore moving away from illness as defining.
3. Therapists' responsibility is to radical collaboration and acceptance.
4. Commitment is to a process, not a clinical outcome. Therapists do not assume responsibility for a client's progress, as this responsibility is shared and learning takes place irrespective of outcome.
5. Effective therapy depends upon understanding sources of distress, not sources of psychosis. It is not necessary to search for causes in order to understand a person's distress and their response to 'psychotic' experiences.
6. Therapists aim is to be themselves more fully with client. Meeting the client as a person (rather than a set of problems) by being a person oneself. By being him/herself more fully the therapist is modelling interpersonal behaviour and reducing the likelihood of the conditional acceptance that the client may routinely experience. Working with people who have 'psychotic' experiences can be stressful. Workers themselves need regular supervision and emotional support in order to maintain an open and collaborative approach towards service users.

Professor Paul Chadwick, Clinical Psychologist [11]

Most of this is common to all good psychological therapy. The different types of therapy have more in common than they have differences. All are essentially an opportunity for a conversation between two or more people, talking through the problems and working out what may be contributing and what might help. A good working relationship between the people involved is vital.

With all psychological therapies it is important to remember that:

- Engaging with therapy is a choice. Where people feel that it is not for them, or not the right time, this should be respected.
- Unlike medication, therapy can only be offered to people, not imposed or forced on them.
- Different people will have different goals for therapy – for example, they may want to address low mood or self-esteem rather than voices or paranoia directly.
- As with other 'treatments', therapy can sometimes have 'side effects' or even do harm.
- Even an excellent therapist will not be a good fit for every client.
- Even the most 'evidence-based' therapies don't help everyone. People themselves are the best judges of whether a particular therapy or therapist is helping them.

There are some differences between approaches, and these are described below. The most researched form of therapy is cognitive behaviour therapy or CBT, and this is discussed first. However, different things suit different people. People may need to try different things to find what works for them.

11.1 Cognitive behaviour therapy (CBT)

CBT (in this context sometimes called CBTp, short for CBT for psychosis) is a structured talking therapy which looks at the way that people understand and react to their experiences.[12]

The experience of CBT

Starting therapy with Paul – the clinical psychologist – was terrifying. I sat, avoiding eye contact, even avoiding looking up from the ground. Often I shook and often jumped at any unexpected sound. I was terrified. But it soon became clear that Paul was not interested in my psychiatric label. And it was also clear he was prepared to address the issue of my voices without belittling them or treating them as weird. The first session the voices were shouting and it was hard to concentrate. Paul recognised this and actually asked me what was going on with the voices. I didn't feel at all 'loony'. Paul made me feel that I was of some importance. Paul spoke – I needed him to speak and put me at my ease. Previously I had seen a psychotherapist who waited for me to speak and often would not reply even when I had braved to utter a word.

The collaborative relationship I have with Paul gives me confidence that my ideas, as well as his, are important. I get to say what I want to work on – I have some power in this relationship. Paul gives me feedback and some idea of his reaction and tells me what areas he might like us to cover. He does this whilst giving me a lot of power and I feel that I am in control.

Talking about the 'voices thing' became open and normal. It has not been shied away from. We have discussed: where the voices come from, the effect they have on me, how the voices feed on my present feelings and how I can, hopefully, partially control them.

We have discussed coping strategies, some successful, some not so, and some just plain silly (humming whilst they are speaking: I could only think of Dionne Warwick songs!). One long-term strategy – challenging the voices – has proved to be the hardest but the most successful. As soon as a voice pops into my head I try to test out, with previous evidence, what the voice is saying. The voices often come up and interrupt sessions. We don't just ignore them, we deal with them.

It now seems to me that the voices always feed off negative images I have about myself. I can think about the voices being a by-product of my own self-image.

Val

The main assumption behind CBT is that distress is at least partly related to the way people interpret, make sense of and respond to things that happen.[13] The therapist empathises with the person's distress and stresses that it is understandable in the circumstances. They try to help the person work out what might be going on, and check out their fears in a safe way. They help the person to identify any vicious circles and how they might be able to avoid or break out of them. The person might begin to make links with things that have happened to them previously. For example, they might realise that traumatic or threatening experiences in their past make them more likely to interpret an event as threatening. They might be able to develop alternative explanations, and perhaps to see patterns – for example that they tend to notice more worrying things when they are already feeling anxious. The therapist works with the person to develop a 'formulation' along the lines described in Section 7 ('How Dan came to understand his problems') to summarise their joint understanding of what might be going on -- including any vicious circles that might be operating – and of possibilities for change. Different people have different goals for therapy depending on their priorities and the nature of their difficulties. The therapist might work with the person to examine and test their beliefs (for example, that someone or something is trying to harm them, or that the voices that they are hearing have power over them). Alternatively, if someone does not wish to examine their beliefs in this way, the therapist might work within the person's own frame of reference to help them find ways to reduce their distress. For example, if someone believes that he or she is being watched by the CIA and does not wish to examine this belief, it might be more useful to think together about coping strategies. The person might try wearing dark glasses, perhaps, so that they feel less anxious about being seen, and can still do necessary things like going shopping.[14]

People might prioritise, and so use therapy to address different problems: for example, low mood, distressing beliefs, distressing voices, how they feel about their experiences and what they mean to them, coping with aspects of life that they are finding particularly hard, or how they feel about themselves.[15] Work is also continuously ongoing to improve and develop therapy and to find ways of helping different people: people in acute crisis and people who want to address longer-term issues, people who hear voices and people who have distressing beliefs, people who are taking medication and those who choose not to, people whose problems are closely linked to their mood, people for whom disrupted sleep is a major issue, people who have problems with alcohol or recreational drugs, people who prefer to come on their own, and people who prefer a group approach.[16,17] As we learn more about the emotional, thinking and other processes that can be involved in different problems, we are able to develop more specific ways of offering help.

Cognitive behaviour therapy

The CBT enabled me to get in control of what was in my head. Everything is less chaotic and my mind is now freed up to do other things.

My therapist was a kind, warm woman and she helped me make maps of my thinking. Just seeing down on paper that my thoughts follow a set course every time was a revelation. Negative thinking is not only seductive, it is a road made of quicksand. You will be swallowed up by it if you give any weight to it. CBT gave me a crossroad to choose from, and I chose positive thinking and action, even though it was easier to water the terrible and beautiful flower that is psychosis… In a nutshell, ten years ago I would have been one of those people who said 'yes, assisted suicide for the mentally ill is a good, necessary thing. But today I don't. Why not? Because I have changed. Change is possible. And if it is possible, how could I possibly advocate assisted suicide?

Dolly Sen [18]

11.1.1 Effectiveness of cognitive behaviour therapy

There is a consistent evidence base suggesting that many people find CBTp helpful.[19,20] Other forms of therapy can also be helpful, but so far it is CBTp that has been most intensively researched. There have now been several meta-analyses (studies using a statistical technique that allows findings from various trials to be averaged out) looking at its effectiveness. Although they each yield slightly different estimates, there is general consensus that on average, people gain around as much benefit from CBT as they do from taking psychiatric medication.[21,22,23,24,25,26]

Although psychological therapies don't help everyone, for others they can make a huge difference to their lives.[27] Even where they don't reduce the frequency or intensity of experiences, they often help reduce distress, which of course is what many people are hoping for. They can also help people to find ways of achieving their goals and getting on with their lives even if their experiences (for example voices) continue. Sometimes changes are even visible in neuroimaging studies (scans) of the brain.[28]

The National Institute for Health and Care Excellence (NICE) considers the evidence strong enough to recommend that everyone with a diagnosis of schizophrenia should be offered CBT. NICE recommends that people should be offered at least 16 one-to-one sessions over a minimum of six months.[29] However, this is far from being the case everywhere: indeed the Schizophrenia Commission found that only one in ten people who could benefit from it have access to good CBTp[30]. We view this with grave concern – indeed, it has been described as scandalous.[31]

There is now a competence framework which describes the knowledge and skills needed by practitioners of CBTp.[32] There is consensus about some of the necessary 'active ingredients',[33] which are reflected in the competence framework. Without them, therapy has the potential to be unhelpful or even damaging. They are listed in the text box, together with quotes from people who have experienced them as part of therapy.

The necessary 'active ingredients' of CBT for psychosis

Offering choice over when and whether to undertake therapy:

To be honest there would have been times where there was no way I would have engaged with it or benefited from it... I think you've got to be ready and motivated for it because there is quite a lot of thinking and you need to be fairly open minded.

Collaboration:

It was very much a partnership between myself and the psychologist. It was really put to me as team work, which I thought was great. It wasn't that someone else has an agenda... it was centred around me which I'd not come across before.

Not seeing psychotic experiences as crazy or wrong:

...all these thoughts, I was thinking when I felt fine, oh my god they're crazy but [therapist] helped me to see that the thoughts weren't crazy, after looking at what happened.

Using formulations to understand the links between thoughts, feelings and behaviour:

...like maps of my mood and little things about different parts of your life and how they can fit together. He would draw little diagrams that made sense to me and I'd be like 'Yeah, yeah, you're right'.

Examining and testing out ways of thinking:

I think the evidence thing's kind of good... you have to sort of work out 'Well, is it likely to be real?' Like if you think, say, people taking thoughts out of my head... well what's the proof that they are?

Trying things out in the real world between therapy sessions:

I feel if I hadn't done the homework that I had, then, and showed up to the sessions as well, I think it would have taken me a lot longer.

All quotes from interviews by service user researcher Martina Kilbride and colleagues [34]

11.1.2 Less formal support drawing on CBT related ideas

Even though unfortunately the majority of service users in the UK still have no access to CBT or indeed any formal talking therapy, they do all have conversations with mental health workers. The ideas contained in this report, including those drawn from CBT, can be very useful in informing those conversations. Part of the motivation for writing this report was to make the ideas more widely available. We hope that all workers will read and discuss it as part of their training, and that families and friends will use it to inform their conversations.

Mental health staff can help people identify and implement strategies, perhaps ones that others have found helpful,[35] or which are used by self-help groups such as the Hearing Voices Network. Examples might include:

- *'Coping strategy enhancement'* whereby people build upon their own repertoire of ways of coping such as listening to music, exercise or standing up to voices.[36]
- *'Behavioural activation'* and *'activity scheduling'* – these involve planning your time and increasing activity levels, strategies which many people have found helpful.[37]
- Problem solving – identifying a specific problem, identifying possible solutions, choosing one to try, and then reviewing how it went.
- Finding ways to reduce stress.
- *'Relapse prevention'* – people who have experienced crises in the past identify warning signs and how to act on them to reduce the likelihood of future crises.
- Focusing on sleep. Poor sleep and insomnia can lead to, or increase problems such as paranoia. Strategies focused on bedtime routine, relaxation and being active in the daytime can decrease both insomnia and paranoia. Many people find this approach helpful, sometimes more so than addressing the paranoia directly.[38,39]

At the moment the biggest evidence base is for CBT. However, other approaches can also be helpful and many of these are currently being researched to find out how many people they help, how, to what extent, and how they can be improved. Some are described below.

11.2 Cognitive remediation

In addition to experiences such as voices or paranoia, some people experience problems with structuring their thoughts or with memory, problem solving or planning. An approach called 'cognitive remediation' has been developed which addresses these problems directly. It can help with 'real life' challenges such as finding and keeping a job[40,41] and can sometimes be useful alongside other psychological therapies, reducing the number of sessions people need.[42]

11.3 Trauma focused therapy and psychodynamic approaches

As we saw in Section 6, many people who hear voices or feel paranoid have survived traumatic or abusive experiences, and so it can be helpful for therapy (including CBT) to focus not only on the here-and-now but also on the psychological effects of trauma. Many psychologists are skilled in working therapeutically with people who have survived trauma, including working with flashbacks and dissociation (dissociation means mentally distancing yourself from what is happening, a common way that people cope with trauma). As we saw in section 6, there is a great deal of overlap between these experiences and 'psychosis': indeed there have been suggestions that they are essentially the same thing.[43] Psychologists have adapted trauma-focused approaches to therapy in order to help people who experience psychosis.[44,45,46,47]

Psychodynamic therapy also attends to how things that have happened in our lives continue to affect us. This approach focuses both on difficult things that have happened and also on our relationships, including the way we relate to ourselves as well as to others.

> After much searching, she finally encounters truly wise people, brave souls who have the courage and integrity to witness her truth. As much as it pains them, they listen to her stories from the underworld, and hear of the terrible suffering that many children have endured. Together they walk down a long winding, road, back to the underworld, where a process of truth and reconciliation, of listening, bearing witness and of facing the horrors of the past can take place. The world will never look the same again to them for they have seen the underworld. And even though she is a freak of nature they love her and they hold her and they soothe her and gradually she begins to feel human. She begins to feel real. She discovers that she isn't alone in quite the same way that she always had been. She begins to accept support as an act of courage and commitment to life and the future. Only then can she begin to truly mourn for all she has lost. She did not know it was possible to cry so many tears... then one day she suddenly knows what she has always known. Her voices are more than just voices. They are many different selves, with different names, ages, experiences, feelings, identities; dissociated selves that became internal representations of her external world. Rather than trying to eradicate these different parts of her even though they sometimes frighten her, she begins to embrace them. Each is part of the whole of her. She begins to listen to them and understand them and to greet them with compassion and understanding. To her delight, they begin to teach her the mysteries of healing, alchemy and magic. Gradually she feels less ashamed of who she is and begins to marvel at how creative she has been in surviving the horrors of the underworld.
>
> Jacqui Dillon, from The Tale of An Ordinary Girl [48]

11.4 Acceptance and commitment therapy and mindfulness

Some people find using mindfulness meditation helpful, or the related approach of acceptance and commitment therapy.[49,50] These approaches involve noticing or becoming more aware of thoughts and experiences and accepting them as things that come and go, as just thoughts rather than as facts. Some psychologists now offer guided mindfulness sessions tailored to the needs of people who have experienced psychosis.[51,52] Acceptance and commitment therapy (ACT) is based on the idea that we all experience distress, and that rather than putting our energy into fighting and trying to control it, it can help if we are able to develop acceptance of our emotional pain and focus on what is important to us. Many psychologists draw on these ideas alongside those described above.

11.5 Narrative and systemic therapies

The idea behind narrative therapy is that our lives and identities are shaped by stories that we develop about ourselves and that others develop about us.[53] Narrative therapy groups help their members to fully describe their rich stories and to overcome the effects of narrow and negative stories that are told about them (for example, being a 'chronic schizophrenic'). An example is the

Power to our Journeys group described by narrative therapist Michael White.[54,55] Similarly, systemic therapy emphasises the role played by the 'systems' that we are part of, such as our families or wider society. It looks at the ideas, beliefs and stories that are around within them, and how we each negotiate our place and our relationships. It can often be useful for family meetings (section 9.1.1.1) to draw on these ideas.

> When you're in the acute phase you're lost in your experiences and in the mythic story that you've developed to make sense of them. You need help to navigate them. The nature of this story, the meaning it provides and your relationship to it (how true is this and how do I tell what is truth?) is key to developing a way of living successfully, or not, and recovering well or not. Essentially the medical model is a very successful story that is offered to people and comes with supporting goods of medication and the mythology of the psychiatrist and his skills. (This is not to say that this story or mythology is all myth.) Of course, having just this story and meaning for the experiences is not helpful. It rules out other meanings which are important – particularly the important one that we have responsibility for our own complex story and medication is not usually going to solve the whole problem.
>
> Laura Lea, Contributor

11.6 Voice dialoguing

Voice dialoguing is a relatively new approach which can be helpful for some people who hear distressing voices. It is based on the idea that the different voices often reflect different aspects of ourselves or experiences we have had. A therapist (called a 'facilitator' in this context) asks questions of the different 'voices' in order to help the person explore, and if helpful to change, their relationship to them.[56] Some researchers are exploring using avatars to represent voices.[57]

11.7 Helping families

Section 9 described the ways in which services can help family and friends to support someone, including offering regular meetings where the whole family can discuss things. There is now very good evidence that many people find such 'family interventions for psychosis' extremely helpful.[58,59,60,61] NICE recommends that this kind of help should be offered to everyone with a diagnosis of psychosis or schizophrenia who lives with or is in close contact with family members, together with particular support for the family members who are most closely involved in helping their loved one.[62]

11.8 Increasing Access to Psychological Therapy

Unfortunately, despite the high demand for psychological therapy and the evidence of its effectiveness, services have been slow to catch up and the vast majority of people still have no access to it. Despite NICE recommendations,[63] there are still many, many service users who request therapy and for whom it might even be lifesaving, but who cannot access it on the NHS. Even those who do have often waited for years: Dolly Sen, for example, talks about a 'wasted decade' of her life before she was offered psychological therapy.[64]

National Institute for Health and Care Excellence (NICE) recommendations:

Services should:

- 'Offer cognitive behavioural therapy to all people with psychosis or schizophrenia. This can be started either during the acute phase or later, including in inpatient settings.'
- 'Offer family intervention to all families of people with psychosis or schizophrenia who live with or are in close contact with the service user. This can be started either during the acute phase or later, including in inpatient settings.'[65]

In 2012 the influential 'Schizophrenia Commission'[66] noted that 'It is unacceptable that only 1 in 10 of those who could benefit get access to true CBT, despite it being recommended by NICE.' Many service user groups and mental health charities are also actively campaigning for talking therapy to be more widely available.[67] The government has expressed its intention to 'improve access to psychological therapy for severe mental illness'[68] but currently only a few sites are funded. More investment is urgently needed.

In February last year, 10 years since being diagnosed, I finally started psychological therapy treatment. I went to the Maudsley Hospital in London every week for sessions of CBT and the therapist helped me to find strategies to cope. I have really bad problems sleeping and CBT has helped with this and really helped with the 'nasty voice'. CBT has helped me remain aloof from this voice and I no longer believe what it says. I now think of the voice as a petty bully and don't let it bother me. It's all about taking back control. The difference CBT has made is amazing – it has really transformed my life ... The only thing I regret is that I didn't have access to it sooner – it could have prevented a lot of suicide attempts and I wouldn't have felt so awful for so long.

David Strange [69]

11.9 Finding an approach that suits you

Although nearly everyone benefits from talking about their experiences, and many people benefit from formal psychological therapy, this is not the case for everyone. Some people prefer more informal support from friends, family and mental health staff.

As with medication, it is possible for therapy to do harm as well as good.[70] It can be difficult to talk about painful issues. Sometimes people receive incompetent or inadequate therapy, or even meet abusive therapists. It is an unfortunate but very real fact that a small number of people in every profession sometimes cross the boundary into inappropriate behaviour. NHS Trusts, professional bodies such as the British Psychological Society, the Health and Care Professions Council and the police rightly take such abuses very seriously.

People from ethnic and other minority backgrounds may find it particularly difficult to find a therapist who is sufficiently aware of our culture and of the specific issues we may face.[71,72] As we noted earlier, western mental health services have sometimes ignored the fact that different cultures have different frameworks of understanding with respect to the nature and origins of mental health problems, and what is likely to help.[73] Western approaches to therapy tend to assume that the causes of people's problems lie in their mind or brain, and require help from outside experts. However, not everyone sees things in this way and many people might see distress as say, more related to spiritual conflicts, or as arising from the need to make changes in society or acknowledge past hurts. They may place an emphasis on the role of the family, community elders or healers. There is a debate about how much Western approaches to therapy can usefully be adapted.[74,75]

Different types of therapy also suit different people. People may need to try more than one approach, and professionals need to respect people's decisions.

11.10 Conclusions

There is now overwhelming evidence that psychological approaches can be very helpful for people who experience psychosis. However, there remains a wide variation in what is available in different places. Even the most successful approaches, such as early intervention and family work, are often not available, and nine out of ten of those who could benefit have no access to CBT.[76] There is a pressing need for all services to come up to the standard of the best and to offer people genuine choices.[77] Perhaps most importantly, we need a culture change in services such that the psychological understanding described in this report informs every conversation and every decision.

Section 12: Medication

Key points

Many people find that 'antipsychotic' medication helps make experiences such as hearing voices less intense, frequent or distressing. It can be particularly useful at times of crisis when the experiences can feel overwhelming.

However, the drugs appear to have a general rather than a specific effect: there is little evidence that they are correcting an underlying biochemical abnormality.

There are significant risks as well as potential benefits, especially when people take medication over many years.

Prescribers need to help people to weigh up the risks and benefits of taking particular drugs or indeed taking medication at all. People need to be able to try things out and arrive at an informed choice. Services should not pressurise people to take medication.

As we saw in Section 11, psychological therapies are still often not offered routinely. However, nearly everyone who comes to services for help with voices or unusual beliefs is offered medication. The most commonly prescribed drugs are those known as neuroleptics. These drugs (sometimes called 'antipsychotics' or major tranquillisers) were first developed in the late 1940s and have since been widely used to try and reduce 'psychotic' experiences. There are many types, including chlorpromazine, thioridazine, trifluoperazine, sulpiride, haloperidol, flupenthixol and fluphenazine. More recently, newer neuroleptics (for example, clozapine, risperidone, quetiapine and olanzapine) have come into use. These are often referred to as 'atypical antipsychotics'.

12.1 How can medication help?

Many people find neuroleptic medication helpful, particularly in acute crises when experiences can feel overwhelming. They can reduce the intensity of experiences and help make them less distressing. Some people also find them helpful for a period afterwards, or even long-term, to make the experiences feel more manageable and reduce the likelihood of them increasing in severity or intensity.

Whilst there is no doubt that many people find neuroleptic drugs helpful, there is some controversy over how they work. Many appear to affect the neurotransmitter (brain chemical) dopamine,[2] and they are sometimes thought of – and often promoted by pharmaceutical companies – as specific treatments for specific illnesses, perhaps by correcting some sort of chemical imbalance. However, this idea is contested, and it has been suggested that the term 'antipsychotic' is rather misleading.[3] In practice what they do appears to be more general, exerting a 'damping down' effect on thoughts and emotions[4] in a comparable way to other psychoactive drugs such as diazepam (Valium).[5] This can of course be very useful, particularly when someone is very agitated or is experiencing many distressing thoughts. Some psychiatrists are now suggesting adopting a 'drug-centred' rather than a 'disease-centred' approach.[6] What this means is that medication can sometimes be helpful for people who are in distress, but that is not the same as curing an illness or putting right a biochemical abnormality or imbalance.

As with psychological therapies, some people benefit massively from taking medication and others not at all. With both types of treatment, professionals should provide information about what is available and about what research suggests others have found helpful. Then we need to support people to try things and see what works for them.

People who find neuroleptic medication helpful

With the new medication I felt as sane as anyone, quite refreshed in mind, and wanted to go home immediately. As if by magic, the psychosis was finished – it was as though an unbearable and excruciating horror film had suddenly, in a flash, been revealed as only a dream.

Peter Chadwick [7]

It was vital to my own recovery that I had the insight and humility to accept that I had had an illness... a real malfunction at cognitive and brain hardware level... The experience of medication was also such that there has never been any feeling that it has turned me into someone I am not; on the contrary, I always have felt that haloperidol removed all the barriers that were preventing me from being who I am. From a nomadic life of faux pas and embarrassments by the dozen, the moment I was switched ... from chlorpromazine to haloperidol and the latter medication 'hit' at neural level, I instantly could feel the change in mental state within – even though I was sat on an empty bus... As the bus pulled away from the terminus stop, the drug started to be active. 'It's all over', I thought to myself. I have never really looked back from that moment. The problems with my attentional style and arousal and emotion modulation were corrected instantly. I could feel it immediately, even on a deserted bus. I stepped off that vehicle later in West London with a radically different and, as far as I am concerned, 'corrected' brain from the one I had when I stepped on it. I have dutifully taken this medication now for 25 years.

Peter Chadwick [8]

The drug blocks out most of the damaging voices and delusions and keeps my mood stable.

Anonymous [9]

Medication is a necessary evil as I have very little to fall back on otherwise. The medication stops psychotic symptoms, or has in the past.

Anonymous [10]

To improve my health I needed medication – the one that suited me and had the least amount of side effects possible. I still have an ambivalent response to my medication. After many years of chopping and changing medication, I finally found one that helped me... Although I feel extremely uncomfortable... about the way pharmaceutical companies test on animals and shape mental health policy, I have to acknowledge the drug gave me my life back. Yes, I have tried to stop taking the drug to see if I no longer needed it and found the psychosis was still there.

Dolly Sen [11]

12.2 Problems with 'antipsychotic' medication

12.2.1 Effectiveness

Until recently the 'received wisdom' has been that everyone who experiences psychosis should take medication long-term to reduce the likelihood of 'relapse'.[12] However, opinion on this is changing. An editorial in the *British Journal of Psychiatry* has suggested that the general effectiveness of 'antipsychotic' medication may have been over-estimated.[13] A meta-analysis (which pools results from many studies) suggested that many people experience only slight benefits and only about 20 per cent experience a significant improvement or prevention of reoccurrence. There appears to be little difference in this regard between 'old' and the 'new' types of medication.[14] Recent studies which followed people's recovery over seven to 20 years found that although in the short term they had more relapses, in the longer term people who reduced their dose or were able to cope without taking medication tended to do better.[15, 16]

12.2.2 Unwanted effects

Most drugs have unwanted effects (also called adverse effects or side effects) as well as desired ones. Common unwanted effects of 'antipsychotic' medication include stiffness, weakness and tremor ('parkinsonism'), tension and restlessness ('akathisia') and muscle spasms. Trials with healthy volunteers have suggested that neuroleptic medication can also cause the tiredness, apathy and lethargy which are sometimes considered 'negative symptoms of schizophrenia'.[17, 18] Indeed, in a recent study of people's experiences of taking both 'old' and 'new' types of neuroleptic, the predominant effects that people reported were 'sedation, cognitive impairment and emotional flattening or indifference'.[19] Different drugs have slightly different side effects.[20]

> ## Unwanted ('side') effects
>
> With akathisia there is never any peace from this insistent urge to move, be it rock backwards and forwards in a chair, shuffle around the wards, kneel and huddle in a chair or go for a walk. It is like a tinnitus of the body; there is never a moment of inner silence. I remember one day staring into a mirror on Ward 3. My eyeballs were bulging, my skin was greasy and grainy, my hair like rats' tails, I was stiffened and troubled by constipation and simultaneously racked by akathisia. I looked like everybody's image of a mental patient – but it was entirely a medication effect.
>
> Peter Chadwick [21]
>
> After trying plenty of neuroleptics at the maximum dosages (one was even put even higher) I was being labelled as treatment resistant. I was now taking five different medications every night before bed. I entered hospital at 19 years of age, 5ft 8in and 8 stone 7 lbs. I now weighed 16 stone 7lbs (clinically obese). I used to enjoy running but now walking up a flight of stairs was exhausting. In fact, being awake was exhausting. I was so sedated that I would sleep at any opportunity I could (I even fell asleep at the dinner table a couple of times). I became incontinent; unable to sleep through the night without wetting the bed (and I didn't even realise until the morning because I was in such a comatosed sleep). I then began wetting myself at work and so had to quit because I wasn't prepared to wear nappies.
>
> Sally Edwards

An issue that has caused controversy recently is that of the likely effects of neuroleptics when they are taken – as they often are – for many years. Some people find it helpful to take them long-term, and in the past services have often recommended that people should do so if they have had a significant 'psychotic' episode. However, recent research suggests that long-term use can sometimes lead to health problems such as decreased brain volume[22] or heart problems.[23] This has created a dilemma for prescribing clinicians. A leading researcher has recently concluded that clinicians should prescribe them at the 'lowest possible dosages'.[24] Many people gain weight, and of course being overweight brings its own problems and risks such as diabetes. Recent evidence suggests when used long-term, unwanted effects can outweigh positive effects for many people.[25] This is particularly important in view of the increasing evidence that people with a diagnosis of schizophrenia have a significantly lower average life expectancy than others.[26] The likely reasons for this are complex, including increased suicide risk, frequent poverty and poorer physical health care (there is evidence that health care workers can be prejudiced and sometimes miss problems). Whilst one study found that taking psychiatric medication appeared to increase average life expectancy,[27] for many people the opposite may be true.[28] Science journalist Robert Whitaker has drawn attention to these issues in his books *Mad in America* [28] and *Anatomy of an Epidemic.*[29]

Being on medication can also have psychological effects. For example, the idea that it is medication that makes things better can give the misleading message that there is little that people can do to help themselves. It is important that workers think of, and present, medication as only one of many things that might help.[30]

People who find neuroleptic medication unhelpful

They do not cure the causes of conditions; they have the side effects of making you unnaturally doped, enormously fat.

Anonymous [31]

I am trying to get off the medication... I don't want to be like a zombie for the rest of my life.

Frank Bruno [32]

It did help me, but my personality has been so stifled that sometimes I think the richness of my pre-injection days – even with outbursts of madness – is preferable to the numbed cabbage I have now become ... in losing my periods of madness I have come to pay with my soul.

Anonymous comment on taking a long-acting ('depot') injection [33]

Things blur with medication. Large chunks of time disappear into black holes, parts of the story of your life, ripped out like censored pages of a book. The very part of the story you wish to read has gone, forever. Crippling side effects that scared the living daylights out of me – I had them all, and I couldn't handle it. Illness was scary, but not half as scary as its so-called cure. Others may tolerate medication, but for me, there had to be another way.

Amanda Nicol [34]

12.3 Collaborative decisions about medication

Through their training and their work in the field, professionals know what some people have found helpful in the past. However, no prescriber is in a position to know whether neuroleptic medication will help a particular individual, and if so which one, which dose, or taken at which times. Neuroleptics can only be used pragmatically – trying a particular medication and seeing what happens. We need to be honest and take a pragmatic ('suck it and see'), collaborative approach, talking through options and enabling the person to try different things to see what helps.

12.3.1 Weighing up benefits and risks

In the past, when someone has decided to discontinue medication this has sometimes been seen as 'lack of insight' or perhaps as related to suspiciousness or paranoia. However, the *British Journal of Psychiatry* editorial mentioned above[35] suggests that for many people, it may be a rational choice taken after weighing up the risks and benefits. It also suggests that it may be time to reappraise the assumption that 'antipsychotics' must always be the first line of treatment for people diagnosed with psychosis. Finally, it recommends that doctors should prescribe in a more collaborative way, including explicit discussion of the possibility of not prescribing at all. In the past, prescribers have sometimes tended to play down side effects. Given that neuroleptics can be helpful but also often have unwanted effects, it might be useful to think of the decision about taking them as analogous to a decision about undergoing chemotherapy for cancer, in other words weighing the possible benefits against the likely drawbacks. Useful questions to ask might include:

- How do you think the medication is affecting your quality of life?
- What kinds of things it is making it easier or harder to do?
- How might we be able to keep track of its effects?

Recently a number of resources have been developed to provide information and support people in deciding whether to continue taking medication, and to find alternative ways to stay well if they decide to come off or cut down: see the resource list at the end of this report.

> **Important note:**
> It can be dangerous to stop medication suddenly if you have been taking it for some time. Always discuss your decision with a clinician.
>
> See www.comingoff.com[36] or www.mind.org.uk[37] for advice.

12.3.2 Finding the type of medication that suits you best

Finding medication which seems to work best for an individual person, with least unwanted effects, can take time. We all have slightly different chemistries and different people react differently to the same medication. Finding the one that works best involves a process of trial and error. The NICE guideline suggests that if two different neuroleptics have proved ineffective, the person should be offered clozapine.[38] This is because it is believed to work differently and some people find it more helpful. However because it can have serious adverse effects in some people, and so needs close monitoring including blood tests, it is particularly important that the person who will take it makes the final decision.

12.3.3 Working out when to take medication

Many people find medication helpful at those times when experiences are most intense or distressing. Afterwards, some people use them either prophylactically (taking them regularly to try to reduce the likelihood of future episodes) or intermittently (when they feel unwell, distressed or under stress). For some people, prophylactic medication appears to help prevent further distressing episodes and hospital admissions.[39] Many people decide to take it long term to try to avoid these problems. However, this is not the case for everyone and it is important that clinicians help people to test out over time what works for them. It is vital that clinicians respect someone's decision if he or she decides not to take medication or to try coming off, and support the person in this process.

Supporting people to make their own decisions about medication

I took neuroleptics for some time, but then chose to stop taking them because I felt like a zombie. I could no longer even read a book. I do still use medicine, but these days it is more of a maintenance dose with fewer side effects. When voices threaten to overpower me, I increase the dosage temporarily.

Anonymous [40]

At no point during my initial admission was I consulted at all about the medication I was being given. Nobody told me about possible side effects or gave me a chance to engage in decisions about my treatment. My experience was of being treated as a second class citizen, who was expected obediently to take drugs that felt to me very noxious. As the staff were making decisions about me without listening to me I decided not to trust them or their decisions. I was determined to withdraw from the medication at the first available opportunity. It was a very difficult thing to do as the withdrawal effects lasted for many months and included 'rebound' hyperactive states that were interpreted by some as psychotic relapses. It was at least partly as a result of this that I had two further hospital admissions before eventually, at the third attempt, I managed to withdraw successfully from the medication. I did this alone without any support and it was an extremely challenging task. It would have helped if I had been given specialist advice on practical ways to cope with the withdrawal effects. However, mental health workers appeared to assume that if I did not take my medication, I was effectively disengaging from mental health services.

Rufus May [41]

12.3.4 Finding the right dose

Although each medication comes with recommended doses, again it is often a question of the clinician working with the person over time to find the most helpful dose.

There is no evidence that high doses of neuroleptics are more helpful than low doses,[42] but high doses can cause more severe adverse effects. For this reason, the Royal College of Psychiatrists has recommended that high doses should be used only under exceptional circumstances.[43] Current NICE guidelines recommend that only one neuroleptic should be used at any one time.[44] However, high doses and multiple drugs actually appear to be used quite frequently, and this is something we view with concern. An audit by the Royal College of Psychiatrists[45] revealed that one in three people were prescribed more than the maximum recommended daily dose and that 43 per cent of people were on more than one neuroleptic drug.

Part 4: What we need to do differently

Section 13: What mental health services need to do differently

Key points

Fundamental changes are required in the way we plan, commission and organise mental health services.

Services should take as their starting point that mental health is a contested area and should not insist that service users accept any one framework of understanding.

Professionals need to shift from seeing ourselves as treating disease to seeing ourselves as providing skilled help and support to people who are experiencing understandable distress.

Service structures need to allow workers the flexibility to tailor help to the particular needs of each person rather than offering standardised packages of care.

Fundamental changes are needed to many aspects of current services. Whilst some of these can be achieved by individual professionals changing their practice, others require policy changes.[1]

A story

The woman presents her possession, the child, to a man who can only be the devil. Together they laugh and they defile the child and rob her of her innocence... The survival strategies that she unconsciously develops as a child create an illusion of control, an illusion that she has some agency over what happens to her. Despite her abject helplessness, she utilises all the resources available to her at the time – her mind, her body, her spirit – and she fights for her life. She begins to hear voices; voices that talk to her, talk about her, who comfort her, protect her and make her feel less alone. In time, they control and terrorise her but help her to stay alive...

In desperation, she seeks asylum in a place that is meant to provide sanctuary for her... she begins to tell the gatekeepers at the asylum, who assure her that they are learned men, healers in fact, about the children who have suffered in the underworld. To her astonishment, they reiterate the words of the devil. There is no underworld. She is crazy. She is ill. She was born with something wrong with her. She feels as if she has been slapped in the face, kicked while she is down, re-abused. This is insult to injury. She is wild with outrage... The place that is meant to provide her with sanctuary is the place that nearly drives her over the edge once and for all.

Jacqui Dillon, from The Tale of an Ordinary Little Girl [2]

13.1 We need to move beyond the 'medical model'

At least in the UK, most mental health services are currently based on the 'medical model' – the assumption, common in many Western countries, that experiences such as hearing voices indicate illness and result from some sort of problem with the brain. This idea is also enshrined in mental health law and is the basis for compulsion. In the past many professionals have also believed that people experiencing distressing voices or paranoia are unlikely to recover without treatment (usually medication). This belief has led to a perceived 'duty of care' to provide treatment, and a tendency to view someone who does not want the treatment being offered as lacking in insight. As this report has shown, both of these assumptions are unfounded.

This basis needs to change. A more honest and helpful 'guiding idea' for services is this:

Mental health is a contested area. The experiences that are sometimes called mental illness, schizophrenia or psychosis are very real. They can cause extreme distress and offering help and support is a vital public service. We know something about the kinds of things that can contribute to these experiences or cause them to be distressing. However, the causes of a particular individual's difficulties are always complex. Our knowledge of what might have contributed, and what might help, is always tentative. Professionals need to respect and work with people's own ideas about what has contributed to their problems. They need to take into account the person's background and culture, and consider whether their particular life experiences and circumstances (for example poverty, trauma, racism, or homophobia) may have contributed to their difficulties. Some people find it helpful to think of their problems as an illness but others do not. Professionals should not promote any one view, or suggest that any one form of help such as medication or psychological therapy is useful for everyone. Instead we need to support people in whatever way they personally find most helpful, to ensure that the help offered is culturally sensitive and accessible to everyone, and to acknowledge that some people will receive support partly or wholly from outside the mental health system.

These ideas need to guide the whole service, not just the work of clinical psychologists or therapists who work with, but slightly outside of, the main multi-disciplinary team. It is vital that teams change their practice and base all care on a 'team formulation' which includes psychological and social as well as biological aspects of the problem, and is developed in collaboration with the service user.[3, 4] This goes for all types of team: community mental health teams, conventional outpatient clinics, residential or in-patient units including 'psychiatric intensive care', and forensic services.

When people have severe problems or are in crisis and they or others might be at risk, we sometimes have to make difficult decisions. In such situations it is tempting to rely on a simplistic medical model: 'this person has no insight into their illness so they need to be detained and administered medication, by force if necessary'. Of course we need to try to keep people safe. However, in such cases it is all the more important that we try to understand the full complexity of the person's situation, and bring it together in a comprehensive formulation so that we can offer the most appropriate forms of help.

13.2 We need to replace paternalism with collaboration

> ### Collaborative alliance
>
> Clearly, any individual faced with living with serious mental health problems has some very hard thinking to do, some difficult decisions to make and perhaps some risky experiments to try. Anyone in such a situation might value an ally who could help them to work through the issues involved and come to decisions that are right for them. Having decided on a course of action, the person may well then require ... assistance that will enable them to carry through their chosen course and help them to review their decisions from time to time in the light of events. But that is not compliance, rather collaborative alliance.
>
> Dr Rachel Perkins and Dr Julie Repper [5]

In the past services have been based on what might be called a 'paternalistic' approach – the idea that professionals know best and that their job is to give advice. The 'patient's' role is to obey the advice ('compliance'). This now needs to change. Rather than giving advice, those of us who work in services should think of ourselves as collaborators with the people we are trying to help. We can provide general information about what can lead to problems, what can keep them going and what can help – as indeed this report has done. However, each individual is unique and the only way to find out what will help a particular person is to explore their particular situation with them, and then support them to try things.

A trusting, collaborative relationship between the professional and the service user is a necessary prerequisite of, and arguably as important as, any specific treatment. Any treatment (including drug treatment) is unlikely to be very helpful on a long term basis unless the professional and the service user have a positive and meaningfully collaborative relationship.[6] Although effective relationships between staff and service users would seem to be an obvious necessity, services often do not operate as if this were the case.

Every service user needs a worker who enables them to talk and think about their experiences in a calm, supportive and non -judgemental atmosphere, and who is willing to accept – and if necessary work within – their own beliefs about the nature of their experiences. This is perhaps the most important message of this report.

13.2.1 Listening
An essential part of collaboration is listening. Professionals often underestimate the power of simply listening. Careful listening is an essential prerequisite of offering appropriate help, and it is also a powerful form of help in its own right. Many people say that lack of listening is what disappoints them most about mental health services. This is even more the case for people from minority backgrounds whose ideas about mental health may be very different from those of the worker whom they are seeing and whose first language may not be English. It is important that interpreters are available and that services train and employ staff who are familiar with different cultures.

The importance of listening

Only once in 15 years of psychiatric intervention, and at the age of 36, was I able to find someone who was willing to listen. This proved a turning point for me, and from this I was able to break out of being a victim and start owning my experience. The nurse actually found time to listen to my experiences and feelings. She always made me feel welcome, and would make arrangements so that we would not be disturbed. She would switch off her bleeper and take her phone off the hook, and sometimes, as there were people outside her room, she would close the blinds. These actions made me feel at ease. She would sit to one side of me instead of across a desk... Over a six-month period, I was able to develop a basic strategy for coping. The most important thing that she did was that she was honest – honest in her motivations and in her responses to what I told her... Thanks to the support this worker gave, I have been able to develop a range of coping mechanisms.

Ron Coleman [7]

During the five years I spent as a patient, I attempted on a couple of occasions to start talking about the sexual abuse I experienced as a child. I desperately wanted to talk about it and I knew it was necessary. But I was only discouraged from talking about such things. It was always brushed off in the same way my MI5 theories were brushed off. 'The problem with talking about those things is that it will make your symptoms worse' I was told by one therapist.

Sally Edwards

13.2.2 Accepting views other than the illness model

A second key aspect of collaboration is respect for people's beliefs about the nature of their experiences. Some people view their difficulties as a medical illness, some see them as a reaction to things that have happened in their life, some as spiritual experiences, and others as a combination of these. Within Western mental health services, rejection of an illness view has sometimes been seen as 'lack of insight', sometimes even as 'part of the illness'. However, it is unhelpful to insist that people accept any one particular framework of understanding. In particular, professionals should not insist that people agree with the view that experiences are symptoms of an underlying illness. Some people will find this a useful way of thinking about their difficulties and others will not.

Someone who sees his problems as an illness

It was helpful for me to regard myself as having had an illness. This made me respectful of the need to maintain and titrate medication ... the medication has helped me to make more, not less, use of my psychological insight and thus genuinely to gain ground ... It has nonetheless to be said that for this ... to be maintained over years, spiritual, psychosocial and cognitive-behavioural methods were required – otherwise medication dosage would have needed to have been extremely high.

Peter Chadwick [8]

Someone who does not see his problems as an illness

My argument is that the psychiatric system, as currently established, does too little to help people retain control of their lives through periods of emotional distress, and does far too much to frustrate their subsequent efforts to regain self-control. To live 18 years with a diagnosed illness is not incentive for a positive self-image. Illness is a one-way street, especially when the experts toss the concept of cure out of the window and congratulate themselves on candour. The idea of illness, of illness that can never go away, is not a dynamic, liberating force. Illness creates victims. While we harbour thoughts of emotional distress as some kind of deadly plague, it is not unrealistic to expect that many so-called victims will lead limited, powerless and unfulfilling lives.

Peter Campbell [9]

Many people approach services unsure about how best to understand their difficulties. It is important that professionals can reassure them that they are not alone in their experiences and that help is available. However, it is also important not to 'push' one particular view about the cause of experiences, whether this is a biological one (that experiences are something to do with the working of the brain) or indeed a psychological one (that experiences are something to do with the way we think). We need to remain open-minded, give people information (a copy of this report perhaps) and support them in coming to their own understanding of their unique situation. Other people who approach services – or in some cases receive them against their will – have already arrived at a particular understanding of their difficulties and do not wish to discuss this. In such cases, whilst providing information, we need to respect and work collaboratively with the person's frame of reference. This is particularly important when working with people from different cultures or minority backgrounds. It contrasts with the traditional approach which might have seen this as 'colluding with delusions'.

Working within the person's frame of reference/belief system

Even from the very first session I had with (clinical psychologist) I felt a huge sense of relief. My 'symptoms' became experiences again and rather than discouraging me to talk/engage/ entertain them, he actively encouraged this. He wanted to get to know the voices I was hearing using voice dialogue. Just a space to talk in detail about every quality of my voice hearing experience to someone that wanted to listen was enough to shift things. Rather than telling me that the beliefs I had were delusions that I should stop believing he asked all about my beliefs. He focussed on how these beliefs made me feel and how I could live whole heartedly within these beliefs. There was never a point were I was told what I experienced was wrong, illogical or meaningless and there was CERTAINLY no agenda to get rid of my experiences, rather, the aim was to get to know them...

Through writing I was able to begin sharing with (clinical psychologist) the sexual abuse I experienced as a child and young adult. He helped me to understand what had happened and understand and express how I felt about it. I had to begin to try and find myself not guilty and give the shame I felt back to its rightful owner... the abusers. When I started to express the rage, shame, fear and deep sadness I had bottled up, my voices began to calm down and give me an easier time.

Sally Edwards

Last week at the ward round we decided to get someone a rape alarm. She believed that she was being raped in the night on the ward. It's a women-only ward and the staff are really confident no one is getting into her room. The staff think the beliefs are delusional. Nevertheless we are getting her the rape alarm – working within her frame of reference and we anticipate this may reduce her stress at night and help her recovery – it will also help if we can move her off the acute ward!

Dr Sara Meddings, Clinical psychologist

Although your friends probably cannot hear or see what you can, it's possible for them to understand and accept your reality and address it in a way which respects your experience.

Example: 'When a snake has entwined itself around my body, if I describe its exact size and location, my friend can pull it off me, even though he can't see it'

Anonymous [10]

My views and beliefs were wrongly interpreted as an illness. If the professionals concerned had taken the trouble to consult with people from my own cultural background the facts would have been perfectly clear to them. After release from hospital, under heavy medication, I was escorted on an aircraft by a British doctor and returned to Nigeria, where I was not seen as ill but received the spiritual help I needed and weaned off medication. I finally returned to the UK and now am a practicing itinerant pastor/evangelist.

Naphtali Titus Chondol [11]

13.2.3 Collaboration rather than just 'involvement'

Professionals must listen to what service users and former service users have to say about services and treatments – it is only by listening that we can learn what really is helpful. It should be standard practice for service users to be involved at all levels, from planning the service as a whole to providing feedback to individual teams and, perhaps most importantly, in planning their own care.[12] Lived experience of mental health problems should be recognised as an important source of knowledge alongside 'book-learning' for professionals.[13] As some NHS Trusts already do,[14] services should see personal experience of mental health problems as 'desirable' in their selection criteria for staff, including senior clinicians. We also need to work with different communities - for example faith and cultural groups, groups representing older people, people on low incomes or sexual minorities - to understand the barriers they face in accessing help and ensuring that services are appropriate to their needs.

13.3 We need to stop telling people what to do and start supporting them to choose

13.3.1 Trying things out

Professionals need to acknowledge that the only way someone can find out for sure what helps them personally, is to try things out. Our role is to provide information about what is available and what others have found helpful, and then support people to choose. Given the problems with 'diagnoses' outlined above, it is important that specific diagnoses (e.g. schizophrenia) are not required in order to access services. We welcome the fact that guidance on how services should be organised (into 'clusters' and 'pathways') takes this approach.[15] However, we view with concern the increasing emphasis on delivering set 'packages of care': workers need the flexibility to work with each service user to meet his or her unique needs.[16]

13.3.2 Talking therapy

It remains scandalous that despite the NICE recommendations, still only a minority of people are offered talking therapy.[17] Psychological help should be available to all, as should help for family members who support people experiencing psychosis. People should have a choice of therapists so that they can find someone with whom they feel comfortable and who they feel understands the issues they are facing. This is particularly important for people from disadvantaged minority groups who often have difficulty accessing therapy,[18,19] or find that therapists do not have sufficient awareness of their background or the particular issues they are likely to face.[20,21,22] Wherever possible people should be able to access services specifically for those who share their particular background or experiences.[23,24,25,26]

13.3.3 Medication or no medication

Service users and their supporters have the right to information about the pros, cons, possible adverse effects ('side-effects') and evidence base for any medication that is offered. Particularly when contemplating taking medication long-term, people should be encouraged and supported to ask questions about the drugs and any alternatives. Professionals need to be open about the fact that prescribing is pragmatic: finding out whether medication is likely to help someone, and if so which drug and dose, is always a trial-and-error process. We also need to provide information about the best way to come off medication if that is what the person wants to do, and to support them in the process.

13.3.4 Professional help, peer support or self-help

As we explained above, many people will prefer community-based or self-help approaches to any kind of professional treatment. Professionals need to give people information about groups affiliated to organisations such as Mind, Bipolar UK, Rethink Mental Illness, Together, Intervoice, the Hearing Voices Network and the Paranoia Network. Groups for people from particular communities are also hugely important, especially given the poor deal that people from minority backgrounds often get from mainstream services. Examples include the Chinese Mental Health Association (www.cmha.org.uk), Sharing Voices[27,28,29] (www.sharingvoices.net) which provides mental health support to diverse minority communities in Bradford and Pink Therapy (www.pinktherapy.com) which offers services to people who are lesbian, gay, bisexual or transgender.

13.4 We need to make rights and expectations explicit

As any treatment has the potential to do harm as well as good, the principle of informed consent is paramount. People should have the right to refuse treatments, from ECT to medication and psychological therapies.

Every service should publish a statement explicitly setting out what users can expect .[30]
The details of what is possible will vary from service to service, but the key thing is to make them explicit. NICE has listed what people have a right to expect in UK mental health services.[31]

Example:
A public statement by a community service about what people who use it can expect

As a client you have the right to:

- Receive respectful treatment
- Receive treatment appropriate to your cultural background
- Refuse treatment or a particular intervention strategy
- Ask questions at any time
- Know your worker's availability and waiting period
- Have full information about your worker's qualifications including registration, training and experience
- Have full information about your worker's areas of specialisation and limitations
- Have full information about your worker's therapeutic orientation and any technique that is routinely used
- Have full information about your diagnosis, if used
- Consult as many workers as you choose until you find one you are happy with
- Experience a safe setting free from physical, sexual or emotional abuse
- Agree to a written contract of treatment/care
- Talk about your treatment with anyone you choose, including another worker
- Choose your own lifestyle and have that choice respected by your worker/s
- Ask questions about your worker's values, background and attitudes that are relevant to therapy and to be given respectful answers
- Request that your worker/s evaluate the progress of therapy/treatment
- Have full information about the limits of confidentiality
- Have full information about the extent of written or taped records of your therapy/ treatment and your right of access
- Terminate therapy/treatment at any time
- Disclose only that personal information that you choose
- Request a written report on therapy/treatment
- Have access to any written summaries about your therapy/treatment.

13.5 We need to reduce the use of compulsion and mental health legislation

13.5.1 Changing the culture of psychiatric hospitals

Mental health wards can be aversive places to be, particularly for anyone who does not think of their difficulties as an illness. This is probably the main reason that mental health legislation has to be invoked so frequently to keep people in hospital. Being admitted to hospital, especially against one's will, is also often in itself a traumatic experience, inadvertently further traumatising people.[32,33] We need to create places that people want to go to when they are in a crisis, that treat everyone equally, and where care is informed by the approach outlined in this report. Acute wards need to change so that they operate on the principles outlined here. Every district should also have at least one non-medical crisis house.

There is a need to address institutional racism within services. The MacPherson Inquiry into the murder of Stephen Lawrence[34] defined institutional racism as the 'collective failure of an organisation to provide an appropriate and professional service to people because of their colour, culture, or ethnic origin...it can be seen or detected in processes, attitudes and behaviour which amount to discrimination through unwitting prejudice, ignorance, thoughtlessness and racist stereotyping which disadvantage minority ethnic people'. These processes can happen even if people in the institution do not individually hold racist beliefs or act in an overtly racist manner. A number of reports have identified key changes needed in order to improve mental health services[35,36] and recently there have been calls for commissioners to play a more active role in rectifying 'ethnic inequity'.[37]

> The inadequate care that many people with psychosis receive adds greatly to their distress... Most have a period in a psychiatric hospital unit but too many of these wards have become frightening places where the overwhelmed nurses are unable to provide basic care and support. The pressure on staff for increased 'throughput' means that medication is prioritised at the expense of the psychological interventions and social rehabilitation which are also necessary. Furthermore, some wards are so anti-therapeutic that when people relapse and are in need of a period of care and respite, they are unwilling to be admitted voluntarily; so compulsion rates rise.
>
> Professor Sir Robin Murray, Chair of the Schizophrenia Commission [38]

13.5.2 Is mental health legislation inherently discriminatory? Is it used fairly?

Many psychologists feel that the existence of separate legislation which applies only to people deemed 'mentally ill' is discriminatory, particularly in view of the problems we have outlined with the whole idea of 'mental illness'. As mentioned above, there are also inequities in the way that the law is applied, with those who already experience discrimination in society, such as homeless people or people from BME backgrounds, also being more likely than others to experience compulsion.

13.5.3 Is forced medication ever justified?

Some psychologists take the view that whilst compulsory detention can sometimes be justified in order to keep someone safe, it is becoming increasingly hard to justify forced medication. The United Nations Special Rapporteur on Torture and Other Cruel, Inhuman or Degrading Treatment has called for a ban[38] on forced psychiatric treatment including drugging, ECT (electro-convulsive therapy), psychosurgery, restraint and seclusion.

Coercion

I am ever ready to support consideration of alternative models of care where there is less emphasis on coercive treatment. I still wake up from nightmares that I have been readmitted and highly medicated against my will. In my community work I recognise the same fear in clients who are desperate to not be misunderstood or judged hospitalisable. This fear of losing one's freedom is a massive obstacle to collaborative mental health care. Where possible, therefore, I believe it is important to not see sectioning and locked wards as given and fundamentally necessary.

Rufus May [39]

13.6 We need to change the way we do research

Firstly, research efforts have been weighted too heavily towards the search for biological abnormalities. The focus of research needs to turn much more towards the events and circumstances of people's lives, and the way that these affect us at a social, psychological and even biological level. We need to understand more about how different things can come together to cause problems, particularly different types of disadvantage such as poverty, homelessness and discrimination,[40,41] and about the links between inequality and mental health. We need to look closely at services too, and in particular at the reasons that people from particular backgrounds appear to get a bad deal[42] in terms of both diagnosis and help.[43,44,45,46,47]

The issue of funding for research is also important. Traditionally, drug companies have funded much medical research into 'schizophrenia'. This raises several important issues. Firstly, this research has often been based on the assumption that the tendency to experience psychosis is primarily a biological phenomenon. As this report has demonstrated, both this assumption and also the view that everyone who has a diagnosis of schizophrenia needs to take medication, are increasingly being challenged. A second issue surrounding drug company funding is one of reliability and bias of findings. Concerns that studies funded by drug companies selectively publish positive findings, and do not publish negative results, have been supported by a number of studies.[48,49,50] The profound effects of the pharmaceutical industry's vested interests have been summarised in a paper called *Drug companies and schizophrenia: Unbridled capitalism meets madness.*[51] There remains an urgent need for more research funding that is independent of drug companies, and for research which focuses on psychological, social and self-help approaches. People from different communities need to be involved in designing and researching more inclusive forms of help.

13.7 We need to change how mental health professionals are trained and supported

Perhaps even more important than the availability of specific talking treatments is the need for all mental health workers to be aware of the information contained in this report. Many workers are unaware of the psychological perspective on psychosis, and are unfamiliar with the research described in this report. A fundamental message of this report is that 'psychotic' experiences are understandable in the same ways as 'normal' experiences, and can be approached in the same way.[52] This message needs to form the core of pre- and post-qualification training. A manual for a two-day training course is available, *Psychosis Revisited*,[53] based on our earlier report and designed to be delivered by a professional in collaboration with someone who has themselves experienced psychosis. Training by people with personal experience is vital, both with regard to how people understand their difficulties, and also with regard to what helps and what doesn't. The Health and Care Professions Council has recently made service user involvement mandatory in professional training courses.[54]

We also need to ensure that training equips mental health professionals to work effectively in an increasingly diverse society, and that the workforce is as representative as possible of the communities it serves. Professionals need to understand the history of discrimination that some people have faced, including racism, sexism and homophobia, and how services can avoid making things worse. Workers also need to learn about the very different ways that those of us from different communities might think about mental health, and the importance of respecting those perspectives rather than imposing their own view.[55,56]

Counsellors and therapists working in primary care or in secondary care psychological services often lack training in working with people who experience psychosis – indeed, often such services specifically exclude people who have experienced psychosis. This needs to change.

These changes need not be expensive. We are suggesting a change in the way that all professionals are trained and approach their work, rather than necessarily recruiting many additional staff. Training costs money, but we are already paying for training, and it needs to change to reflect our developing understanding of the nature of psychosis. What we are recommending is more fundamental than increased resources: a change in the guiding idea behind services.[57]

Finally, staff can only offer the compassion and emotional support that people need when they are themselves supported and shown compassion by their organisation, and when the demands on them are reasonable. It is vital that rather than being quick to criticise, we recognise how demanding mental health work can be and also acknowledge its vital importance in our society.[58]

Section 14: What we all need to do differently

Key points

There is no 'us and them', people who are 'normal' and people who are different because they are 'mentally ill'. We're all in this together and we need to take care of each other.

If we are serious about preventing distressing 'psychosis' we need to tackle deprivation, abuse and inequality.

14.1 We need take on board that we're all in this together – there is no 'us' and 'them'

One of the most important messages of this report is that there is no dividing line between 'psychosis' and 'normality'. There is no 'us' and 'them' – we're all in this together. Many of us hear voices occasionally, or have fears or beliefs that those around us do not share. Given enough stress, for any of us these experiences might shade into psychosis. Sometimes what constitutes 'psychosis' is in the eye of the beholder: for example, if someone does not get on with his or her neighbours, is frightened of them and suspects their involvement when things go wrong, when does this shade into 'paranoia'? The main way that we all need to change is by taking on board that there is no 'us' and 'them', there are only people trying to make the best of our situation.

14.2 We need to focus on prevention

There's no point just mopping the floor and leaving the tap running.

Saying in public health circles [1]

We are working in a society that's creating distress as fast as we can mop it up.

Dr Lucy Johnstone [2]

This report has highlighted the complex causes of distressing psychotic experiences. What is encouraging is that many of the causes are things that we can do something about. There is a parallel here with public health in the physical arena, namely that some of the steps that need to be taken are economic, social and even political. A famous example of the huge difference that public health measures can make is that of Dr William Duncan in nineteenth century Liverpool. As with most doctors in Victorian Britain, Duncan came from a privileged background. But after working as a GP in a working-class area of Liverpool, he became interested in the links between poverty and ill-health and started researching the living conditions of his patients. He was shocked by the poverty he found, and in the clear link between housing conditions and the outbreak of diseases such as cholera, smallpox and typhus. He started a lifelong campaign for improved living conditions, particularly better housing, cleaner water and better drains, which led to huge improvements in the health of many thousands of people. So what might be the mental health equivalent of clean water and sanitation? The evidence suggests that two things are particularly important: safety and equality. These are addressed in the following paragraphs, together with other issues that we need to tackle in order to reduce the rates of mental health problems in our society.

14.2.1 Prevention: safety

To feel safe and secure we need to know that our basic needs will be met. This is why efforts to reduce poverty, and particularly child poverty, are so important if we are to reduce the numbers of people who go on to experience distressing psychosis.

To feel safe and secure we also need to be able to trust those in positions of power over us. In particular, when we are growing up we need to be able to trust the adults who are entrusted with our care. This is why efforts to reduce child abuse and neglect are central to efforts at preventing psychosis as well as other mental health problems. We all need to work with teachers, social workers, community nurses, GPs and the police to identify and then respond to early warning signs that children might be exposed to sexual, physical or emotional abuse, neglect or bullying. As parents we need to seek support ourselves if we worry that our own stress is having an impact on our children. Children who have been exposed to these things need support and nurturing and there is evidence that where this happens, the likelihood of hearing distressing voices later in life, for example, is much reduced.[3]

14.2.2 Prevention: equality

Evidence shows that a major contribution to serious emotional distress is not only poverty but particularly income inequality – the growing gap between the richest and poorest people in society. In their book *The Spirit Level*, sociologists Richard Wilkinson and Kate Pickett demonstrate that mental health problems are highest in those countries with the greatest gaps between rich and poor, and lowest in countries with smaller differences.[4] Equal societies are associated with more trust and less paranoia. This suggests that rather than primarily targeting our efforts at individuals, the most effective way to reduce rates of 'psychosis' might be to reduce inequality in society.

14.2.3 Prevention: reducing discrimination and oppression

A classic paper published in 1994 was entitled *Environmental failure – Oppression is the only cause of psychopathology.*[5] Whilst some might think that goes too far, there is no doubt that people who have been subject to oppression, and particularly discrimination (racism, homophobia, discrimination on grounds of gender, disability or 'mental health') are put at risk by these experiences, and that they can profoundly affect people's mental health. Some experts have argued that they are therefore important public health issues as well as ones of social justice.[6,7,8,9] We can all work to combat discrimination and promote a more tolerant and accepting society.

14.2.4 Prevention: reducing harmful drug use and addressing its causes

Alcohol is unquestionably the most serious substance-related public health issue, but cannabis and other drugs have been associated with mental health problems in general and psychosis in particular. Over-use of recreational drugs appears to make it more likely that someone will experience a psychotic crisis. This does not necessarily mean that we need a stronger clamp-down on drugs – the so-called 'war on drugs' does not appear to have been won, and many people argue that de-criminalising the possession and use of drugs would be an important positive step towards protecting people's health. It is also important to address the social problems that lead people to turn to taking drugs, including poverty, inequality, unemployment, hopelessness and feeling disenfranchised from society.

14.2.5 Prevention: what we can each do to protect our mental health
So far, this section has concentrated on what we can do together to reduce the risk that some of us will experience distressing 'psychosis'. However, research also suggests that there are things that we can each do ourselves to protect our own mental health. Firstly, we can look after ourselves physically: as we saw above, getting regular, good sleep is vitally important, as are nutritious food, exercise, and exposure to open air and green spaces. We can exercise caution with recreational drugs, even very commonplace drugs such as alcohol or cannabis. Since our social environment is also vital, we can usefully examine our relationships with family, friends and colleagues and take steps to resolve sources of stress. Money worries are one of the most common stressors. Although our income is often beyond our control, we can take steps to deal with debt, to plan for retirement, to manage our finances, and to plan for the future (psychologists call this 'adaptive coping'). Finally, we all experience major negative events during our lives, such as when someone close to us dies. Whilst we can't prevent things happening, we have some control over how we respond. For example, do we tend to jump to conclusions or take things personally? Sometimes it can help to talk over with a friend or counsellor how and why we habitually respond the way we do, and any changes we could make. The New Economics Foundation's 'Five Ways to Wellbeing'[10] framework might be of use here.

14.3 We need to campaign against prejudice and discrimination on 'mental health' grounds

This report has shown how we can be affected as much by the reaction of people around us as by the actual experiences themselves. For example, people who are seen as 'mentally ill' often experience prejudice, rejection and social exclusion, which can be significant – sometimes even insurmountable – obstacles to recovery. For many people, prejudice based on misinformation presents a greater obstacle than the original mental health problems.[11] Too many people have been taken in by inaccurate media images and are prejudiced against those with mental health difficulties, wrongly believing them to be incompetent, unreliable, unpredictable, and dangerous.

For many people, the mass media are their major source of information about mental health. However, the way that problems are portrayed is often unhelpful. Unfortunately frightening stories about unusual events have more 'news value'.[12] A second reason is the lack of good information available to journalists. In the absence of other sources of material, they currently often have to rely on court cases and inquiries. Obviously this will lead to a preponderance of stories about crime and tragedy. Alternative sources of material are badly needed, as is training for journalists.

We hope that this report will prove to be part of an ongoing major shift in public attitudes that sees prejudice against people with mental health problems become as unacceptable as racism or sexism.

I have a vision:

That one day I will be able to talk about my mental health problems and attract no more than interest in those around me.

That I can go back to work after a stay in a psychiatric hospital and have my colleagues ask what it was like, rather than delicately avoiding the subject.

That one day we will see a prime minister who openly talks about his or her experience of mental health problems.

Dr Rachel Perkins OBE [13]

Useful books and websites

Websites

www.understandingpsychosis.net
The BPS website where this report can be downloaded for free. There are also links to press coverage, discussion and debate.

First person accounts and service user/survivor websites

www.asylumonline.net
'An international magazine for democratic psychiatry, psychology and community development.' Features articles written by service users, survivors and professionals.

www.bgmi.us/web/bdavey
Website of survivor Brian Davey. Contains self-help advice based on his own experience, for example about coping with arousal states which might otherwise escalate into a crisis.

www.behindthelabel.co.uk/about
Website of voice hearer Rai Waddingham.

beyondmeds.com
Website and blog of Monica Cassani: 'My own experience as both (now ex) patient and a mental health professional allows for some interesting and sometimes uncomfortable insights into the mental health system in the United States.'

www.bruised.org.uk
Site created by mental health service user and activist Miranda Morland 'to bring information to patients, carers, families and their friends. Knowledge is power. Sadly in the mental health system, the power is usually one-sided. We aim to change this.'

www.ted.com/talks/eleanor_longden_the_voices_in_my_head
Fourteen-minute TED talk: voice hearer and psychologist Eleanor Longden talks about her experiences. 'Longden tells the moving tale of her year-long journey back to mental health, and makes the case that it was through learning to listen to her voices that she was able to survive.'

www.gailhornstein.com
Gail Hornstein is a US professor of psychology. Her website contains a recently updated and comprehensive 'bibliography of first-person accounts of madness in English' together with other resources.

www.healthtalkonline.org/mental_health/Experiences_of_psychosis
Audio and video clips of people talking about their personal experiences of psychosis and about how they understand and cope with them.

www.jacquidillon.org
Website of voice hearer and author Jacqui Dillon.

www.mindfreedom.org

Mind Freedom aims to 'win human rights campaigns in mental health, challenge abuse by the psychiatric drug industry, support the self-determination of psychiatric survivors and mental health consumers and promote safe, humane and effective options in mental health'.

www.mindreel.org.uk/video/only-smarties-have-answer

Only Smarties Have the Answer, a 50 -minute film by Aidan Shingler, an artist who as a young man received a diagnosis of paranoid schizophrenia. He talks about his attitude towards this diagnosis, and satirises mental health services using puppet animation.

www.nationalparanoianetwork.org

Network for people who experience paranoia.

www.selfhelp.org.uk/home

Self Help Connect UK is the new national division of Self Help Nottingham and Nottinghamshire, an organisation which started in the 1980s. It now has about 30 years of experience of self-help and is a unique resource of expertise about how to establish and sustain self-help groups.

Simon Says: Psychosis! www.youtube.com/watch?v=oA0Z33mS1Cg

Excellent short documentary exploring the experience of psychosis and how three young people 'journeyed back from the edge' with help from an early intervention service.

studymore.org.uk/mpu.htm

Website of the Survivor History Group, which aims to document the 'history of individual and collective action by service users/survivors'.

www.recoverydevon.co.uk

A website dedicated to promoting recovery methods and theories to help individuals make an informed decision about their recovery journey.

http://sectioneduk.wordpress.com

'In 2011, I was detained in one of the UK's busiest acute psychiatric hospitals, a brutal and sometimes hilarious introduction to NHS mental health care. You've gotta laugh! ... I set up this blog account six weeks later.' Long list of links to useful resources.

www.voicecollective.co.uk

The Voice Collective is hosted by Mind in Camden and is a resource 'for young people who hear, see and sense things others don't'.

Mental health organisations

www.evolving-minds.co.uk

A West Yorkshire based group, 'Evolving Minds aims to provide a space to discuss, debate, share, learn, value and campaign for alternative and compassionate approaches to emotional and mental health'.

www.hafal.org

Welsh charity dedicated to recovery in mental health. Hafal sees recovery as having three key parts: empowerment and self-management, commitment to progress and a whole person approach. Hafal's website includes information and resources including a step-by-step recovery guide.

www.hearing-voices.org

Mind in Camden's London-wide Hearing Voices Project, linking together Hearing Voices groups across Greater London. Hearing Voices groups are 'a safe place for those who hear, see or sense things that others don't, to meet up with others who understand what they're going through, share their experiences and find creative ways of coping'.

www.hearing-voices.org/groups/lhvn

Mind in Camden's London-wide Hearing Voices Project, linking together Hearing Voices groups across Greater London.

www.theicarusproject.net

The Icarus Project is a grassroots network of independent groups and individuals 'living with the experiences that are commonly labelled bipolar disorder'. It promotes a new culture and language that looks beyond a conventional medical model of mental illness.

www.intervoiceonline.org

Set up by psychiatrists Dirk Corstens and Prof Marius Romme, Intervoice is the international Hearing Voices Network: 'the international network for training, education and research into hearing voices'. The website says: 'Because hearing voices is a much stigmatised experience we wanted to create a safe place where you can find out more about hearing voices and to create an interactive online community where you can let us know about your point of view or experience. We have put together the most extensive international resource on hearing voices you can find on the web. This information includes both ways of overcoming the difficulties faced by people who hear voices, as well as the more positive aspects of the experience and its cultural and historical significance.'

www.isanyoneelselikeme.org.uk

The 'EYE project' – a Sussex-based NHS early intervention project. Information, personal stories and videos aimed at young people.

www.isps.org

International Society for Psychological and Social Approaches to Psychosis: an international organisation promoting these approaches. There is an active UK branch run collaboratively by professionals and people with personal experience of psychosis.

www.mindincamden.org.uk/services/paranoia

The London Paranoia Groups Project is a London-wide project to develop peer support groups for people experiencing paranoia and overwhelming beliefs. The aim is to create safe, supportive groups where people can meet together to share their experiences and learn from one another. Groups provide people with the opportunity to learn to cope with, and recover from, the impact of distressing beliefs.

www.mdf.org.uk
The website of MDF the Bipolar Organisation (formerly the Manic Depression Fellowship), a UK user-led charity for individuals and families affected by bipolar disorder. It includes information about self-help, bipolar disorder and an e-forum. MDF members automatically receive *Pendulum*, the organisation's quarterly journal.

www.mentalhealth.org.uk/help-information
The Mental Health Foundation is a UK charity which provides information, carries out research and works to improve resources for people affected by mental health difficulties with a focus on recovery and wellbeing. The website has a useful help and information section.

www.mentalhealthrecovery.com
Mary Ellen Copeland's website about recovery and the Wellness Recovery and Action Plan (WRAP) approach which is designed to enable people to negotiate with services to design a package of care that is most helpful for them, including plans for any crises. Includes links to resources.

www.meridenfamilyprogramme.com
Resources for friends and families of people experiencing psychosis, and training for professionals in helping friends and families.

www.mind.org.uk
This is the mental health charity MIND's website, which includes useful detailed information about psychiatric medication.

www.mindincamden.org.uk/services/paranoia
The London Paranoia Groups Project is a London-wide project to develop peer support groups for people experiencing paranoia and overwhelming beliefs. The aim is to create safe, supportive groups where people can meet together to share their experiences and learn from one another. Groups provide people with the opportunity to learn to cope with, and recover from, the impact of distressing beliefs.

www.rcpsych.ac.uk
The Royal College of Psychiatrists is the UK professional body for psychiatrists. The website has detailed information and resources for researchers, users of mental health services, the general public and the media.

http://researchintorecovery.com
This is the website of the Section for Recovery at King's College London Institute of Psychiatry. It contains many downloadable resources and information about research on recovery and wellbeing.

www.rethink.org.uk
'Welcome to Rethink Mental Illness. We help millions of people affected by mental illness by challenging attitudes, changing lives.'

www.schizophreniainquiry.org
The Inquiry into the Schizophrenia Label was set up by Jayasree Kalathil, Jan Wallcraft, Suman Fernando and Philip Thomas in order to find out how service users, carers and others perceived the label, and their experiences of it. Over 600 people responded, many of whom said that they found the label unhelpful.

www.sharingvoices.net

Website of the 'Sharing Voices' project in Bradford: 'Mental health experiences often arise from issues around: Poverty, racism, unemployment, loneliness, family conflicts, relationship difficulties and cannot be merely understood through biological terms alone. So listening to people's own explanation and helping them find their solutions to problems is a key part of our work.' The project was set up as a charity using a radical model of community development with a strong commitment to mutual aid.

www.soterianetwork.org.uk/

The Soteria Network is 'a network of people in the UK promoting the development of drug-free and minimum medication therapeutic environments for people experiencing 'psychosis' or extreme states. We are part of an international movement of service users, survivors, activists, carers and professionals fighting for more humane, non-coercive mental health services'.

www.SpiritualCrisisNetwork.org.uk

This website offers an alternative perspective, practical advice and email support to people who are interested in exploring the idea of spiritual crisis. There are some local groups, for example in London.

www.voicecollective.co.uk

A London-based organisation for children and young people who hear, see and sense things others do not.

www.youngminds.org.uk

Young Minds is a UK charity committed to improving the emotional well bring and mental health of young people and empowering their parents and carers. Whilst there is little specific to psychosis on the website, it includes useful information about treatments, campaigns, policies and resources.

Psychologists' websites

www.bps.org.uk/psychology-public/information-public/information-public
Public information section of the British Psychological Society website.

www.bps.org.uk/dcp
Website of the British Psychological Society Division of Clinical Psychology.

https://blogs.canterbury.ac.uk/discursive/
Discursive of Tunbridge Wells: 'Views and commentary on psychology, mental health and other stuff' from the Salomons Centre for Applied Psychology at Canterbury Christ Church University. A frequent theme is how we understand and respond to 'mental illness'.

www.gailhornstein.com
Gail Hornstein is a US professor of psychology. Her website contains a recently updated and comprehensive 'bibliography of first-person accounts of madness in English' together with other resources.

www.dur.ac.uk/hearingthevoice
Led by Prof Charles Fernyhough, Hearing the Voice is 'an ambitious, interdisciplinary research project that aims to provide a better understanding of the experience of hearing voices in the absence of any external stimuli'.

www.isabelclarke.org
This is the website of clinical psychologist Isabel Clarke who writes about spirituality and psychosis. Contact Isabel via the website to request to join an active email discussion group on psychosis and spirituality.

www.paranoidthoughts.com
Website about 'unfounded or excessive fears about others' from Professor Daniel Freeman, clinical psychologist, contributor to this report and author of self-help books (see books section). Includes first-person accounts by people who have experienced suspicious thoughts and paranoia.

http://peterkinderman.blogspot.co.uk
Clinical psychologist and contributor to this report Professor Peter Kinderman's blog. Deals with psychological models of mental health problems, and mental health policy.

www.youtube.com/user/PoeticDocumentarism
Clinical psychologist Dr Rufus May talks about using mindfulness with voices.

www.psychology.org.au/Content.aspx?ID=5101
Australian psychologist Hoa Pham writes about her own diagnosis of schizophrenia and her thoughts on psychological help for 'psychosis'

www.psychosisresearch.com
'The Psychosis Research Unit (PRU) is a joint project between the University of Manchester and Greater Manchester West Mental Health NHS Foundation Trust. PRU was formed in 2008 by Professor Tony Morrison and Dr Paul French. We promote a normalising approach to understanding psychosis. We believe experiences and beliefs commonly regarded as symptoms of psychosis are often highly understandable reactions to adverse life events. Our primary aim is to develop ways of reducing the distress of people with these experiences, as well as developing ways of restoring their autonomy and dignity'.

www.rufusmay.com
Set up by clinical psychologist Rufus May, this website provides a resource of articles, interviews and other media that Rufus has taken part in promoting a positive psychology approach to emotional health and recovery. Includes a paper on 'accepting alternative realities'.

http://treatingpsychosis.com
Set up by clinical psychologist Nicola Wright and others, 'this website is for those who are living with psychosis and for friends, family members, and clinicians of those affected by psychosis. The website's aim is to provide helpful and up-to-date resources including books and research articles, useful websites, downloadable forms, and interactive materials for both clients and clinicians alike'. Beautiful nature photographs too!

www.understandingpsychosis.net
Address for the website associated with this report.

Self-help sites

www.comingoff.com

'This website aims to give you up to date information about psychiatric medication, how it functions and the withdrawal process. It is put together by people who have been prescribed medication and withdrawn from it, and clinicians who have been involved in supporting this process.'

www.livinglifetothefull.com

This is an online life skills resource using CBT principles to help individuals with life difficulties using a cognitive behavioural approach.

www.moodgym.anu.edu.au

A free self-help programme to help people understand and use basic cognitive behavioural therapy techniques for depression and anxiety.

http://theicarusproject.net/HarmReductionGuideComingOffPsychDrugs

From the *Icarus Project* – a guide to coming off psychiatric drugs safely.

Other useful sites

www.asylumonline.net/resources/campaign-for-the-abolition-of-schizophrenia-label
This is a group campaigning to abolish the label 'schizophrenia'.

www.iraresoul.com
This is the website of Daniel Mackler, film maker. Three documentary films are available on DVD about non-medical approaches to helping people through psychosis, for example the 'open dialogue' model from Finland and a Swedish approach which supports families to have people to stay in times of crisis.

http://madinamerica.com
Site run by Robert Whitaker, author of *Mad in America* and *Anatomy of an Epidemic*. 'The site is designed to serve as a resource and a community for those interested in rethinking psychiatric care in the United States and abroad. It provides readers with news, stories of recovery, access to source documents, and the informed writings of bloggers that will further this enterprise.'

www.madnessradio.net
Hour-long radio interviews focusing on personal experiences of 'madness' and extreme states of consciousness. Madness Radio also features authors, advocates, and researchers. For example, there is an interview with psychiatrist Jonathan Metzl about how the term 'schizophrenia' came to be disproportionately applied to young black men: www.madnessradio.net/madness-radio-schizophrenia-and-black-politics-jonathan-metzl/

www.mindreel.org.uk/video/reconnect
This is a 20-minute film about 'Karl', a young man experiencing psychosis who receives help from an early intervention team.

www.undercurrents.org/minds.html
A downloadable film entitled *Evolving Minds* about different perspectives on psychosis.

Online courses

www.futurelearn.com/courses/mental-health-and-well-being
Psychology and mental health: beyond nature and nurture. A course from the University of Liverpool led by Professor Peter Kinderman, a contributor to this report.

www.futurelearn.com/courses/caring-psychosis-schizophrenia
Caring for people with psychosis and schizophrenia. A course from Kings College London.

Training materials

Thurstine Basset, Mark Hayward, Ruth Chandler, Alison Blank, Anne Cooke and Jim Read (2007). *Psychosis revisited – a workshop for mental health workers.* Hove: Pavilion Publishing. Manual for a two-day training workshop for mental health workers based on the our earlier report. The workshop encourages mental health workers to open their minds and take a fresh look at 'psychosis' and how they try to help people who experience it.

Books

First-person accounts of 'psychosis' and receiving services

Basset, T. & Stickley, T. (Eds.) (2010). Voices of experience: Narratives of mental health survivors. New York: Wiley-Blackwell.

This book contains a wide range of stories written by mental health survivors. The narratives illustrate how survivors have developed self-management techniques and strategies for living which, together, offer a guide to anybody struggling with 21st century life.

Cordle, H., Carson, J. & Richards, P. (Eds.) (2010). P*sychosis: Stories of recovery and hope.* London: Quay Books.

Fifteen people tell their stories and professionals describe various approaches to understanding and helping, including the traditional medical mode as well as the recovery approach.

Geekie, J., Read, J. Randal, P.& Lampshire, D. (2011). E*xperiencing psychosis: Personal and professional perspectives.* London: Routledge.

First-person accounts are brought centre stage and examined alongside current research to suggest how personal experience can contribute to the way that professionals try to understand and help.

Millet, K. (1990). *The loony bin trip.* New York: Simon & Schuster.

Kate Millet explores the question of madness, mania and depression, from her own experience. She tells of her struggle with stigma, her forced hospitalisation by family and friends, and her decision to prove her sanity by coming off prescribed medication.

Pegler, J. (2004). *A can of madness. Memoir on bipolar disorder and manic depression: An Autobiography on manic depression.* Brentwood: Chipmunka Publishing.

Jason, now the managing director of Chipmunka Publishing, was diagnosed with bipolar disorder in 1993. He wrote *A Can of Madness* to stop other 17-year-olds going through what he went through.

Pembroke, L. (2004, Kindle Edition 2009). *Self-harm: Perspectives from personal experience.* Brentwood: Chipmunka Publishing.

In this short but powerful book, Louise and others explain how they understand and cope with unusual perceptions and self-harm.

Romme, M., Escher, S., Dillon, J., Corstens, D. & Morris, M. (2009). *Living with voices: Fifty stories of recovery.* PCCS Books.

Fifty people describe how they have overcome their problems with hearing voices outside of the illness model, by overcoming feelings of threat and powerlessness and discovering that voices are not a sign of madness but a reaction to problems in their lives.

Sen, D. (2002). *The world is full of laughter (Memoir on mental distress).* Brentwood: Chipmunka Publishing.

A woman's fight to come to terms with abuse, family pressures, prejudice and mental ill health. Dolly Sen describes the reality and prejudices of being diagnosed with various psychiatric conditions and how she has come through them.

Psychological and social approaches to 'psychosis'

Benamer, S. (2010). *Telling stories? Attachment-based approaches to the treatment of psychosis.* London: Karnac.

'In order to truly understand psychosis we must begin by listening to those who know this from the inside out: the voices and narrative of those who have been condemned as "unanalysable" and mad. Far from being fantastical, the complex stories that are being articulated communicate painful truths and the myriad ways in which the human psyche survives overwhelming trauma.'

Bentall, R. (2004). *Madness explained: Psychosis and human nature.* London: Penguin Books.

Richard Bentall argues that we need a radically new way of thinking about psychosis and its treatment. Could it be that it is a fear of madness, rather than the madness itself, that is our problem?

Chadwick, P. (2006). *Person-based cognitive therapy for distressing psychosis.* Chichester: Wiley.

Provides a practical framework for using a person-based cognitive therapy approach for addressing the range of problems experienced by people with psychosis.

Clarke, I. (2010). *Psychosis and spirituality: Consolidating the new paradigm.* Oxford: Wiley-Blackwell.

Offers a fundamental rethink of the concept of psychosis, focusing on the overlap between experiences that have traditionally been regarded as psychotic and those that have been regarded as spiritual.

Garety, P. & Hemsley, D. (2013). *Delusions: Investigations into the psychology of delusional reasoning.* London: Psychology Press.

'A synthesis which portrays the contribution to date of cognitive science to the biology and psychopathology of delusional thinking.'

Geekie, J. (2009). Making sense of madness: Contesting the meaning of schizophrenia. Hove: Routledge.

This book explores the subjective experiences of 'madness'. Drawing on people's stories and verbatim descriptions, it argues that the experience of 'madness' is an integral part of what it is to be human, and that greater focus on subjective experiences can inform how professionals understand these experience and try to help those who are troubled by them.

Hornstein, G. (2012). *Agnes' jacket: A psychologist's search for the meanings of madness.* Ross-on-Wye: PCCS Books.

'In a Victorian-era German asylum, seamstress Agnes Richter painstakingly stitched a mysterious autobiographical text into every inch of the jacket she created from her institutional uniform. Despite every attempt to silence them, hundreds of other patients have managed to get their stories out... A vast gulf exists between the way medicine explains psychiatric illness and the experiences of those who suffer. Hornstein's brilliant work helps us to bridge that gulf, guiding us through the inner lives of those diagnosed with schizophrenia, bipolar illness, depression, and paranoia and emerging with nothing less than a new model for understanding so-called 'mental illness', one another and ourselves. One which asks not 'what's wrong with you' but 'what happened to you and how did you manage to survive?'

Johnstone, L. (2014). *A straight talking introduction to psychiatric diagnosis.* Ross-on-Wye: PCCS Books.

Psychiatric diagnosis has become one of the most contested practices in mental health services. Lucy Johnstone asks 'Do you still need your psychiatric diagnosis?' She argues that if many mental health workers are openly questioning diagnosis and saying we need a different and better system, then service users and carers should be allowed to do so too.

Johnstone, L. (2000). *Users and abusers of psychiatry: A critical look at psychiatric practice.* London: Routledge.

Using real-life examples and her own experience as a clinical psychologist, Lucy Johnstone argues that the traditional way of treating 'mental illness' can often exacerbate people's original difficulties leaving them powerless, disabled and distressed.

Jones, S., Lobban, F. & Cooke, A. (2010). *Understanding bipolar disorder: why people experience extreme mood states and what can help.* Leicester: British Psychological Society Division of Clinical Psychology.

A companion to the current report, *Understanding bipolar disorder* provides an overview of the current state of knowledge about why some people tend to experience periods of extreme mood and what can help. Much has been written about the biological aspects of 'bipolar disorders'. This report aims to redress the balance by concentrating on the psychological aspects, both in terms of how we understand the problems and also approaches to help and treatment. Downloadable free from www.bpsshop.org.uk/Understanding-Bipolar-Disorder-P1280.aspx

Kinderman, P. & Cooke, A. (Eds.) (2000). *Recent advances in understanding mental illness and psychotic experiences. A report by the British Psychological Society Division of Clinical Psychology.* Leicester: British Psychological Society. Our earlier report which this one replaces and updates.

Knight, T. (2013). *Beyond belief: Alternative ways of working with delusions, obsessions and unusual experiences.* Berlin: Peter Lehmann Publishing.

This book offers a new way of helping people deal with unusual beliefs, encouraging helpers to consider working within, rather than challenging the person's belief system. Downloadable free from www.peter-lehmann-publishing.com/beyond-belief.htm

Lewis Herman, J. (1997). *Trauma and recovery: From domestic abuse to political terror* (revised edn.) New York: Basic Books.

A seminal book about the effects of trauma. The approach that it takes informs many current approaches to 'psychosis'.

McCarthy-Jones, S. (2012). *Hearing voices: The histories, causes and meanings of auditory verbal hallucinations.* Cambridge: Cambridge University Press.
> This book integrates findings from neuroscience with current psychological theories. It considers what may cause voices and makes suggestions for future research.

Razzaque, R. (2014). *Breaking down is waking up: Can psychological suffering be a spiritual gateway?* London: Watkins Publishing.
> Psychiatrist Russell Razzaque argues that what we think of as breakdown can be a spiritual experience.

Read, J. & Dillon, J. (2013). *Models of madness: Psychological, social and biological approaches to psychosis.* London: Routledge.
> 'This second edition challenges those who hold to simplistic, pessimistic and arguably damaging theories and treatments of "madness". In particular it challenges beliefs that madness can be explained without reference to social causes and challenges our preoccupation with chemical imbalances and genetic predispositions as causes of human misery, including the conditions that are given the name "schizophrenia".

Read, J. & Sanders, P. (2010). *A straight talking introduction to the causes of mental health problems.* Ross-on-Wye: PCCS Books.
> Suitable for mental health service users, their carers, students and mental health professionals, this book presents an introduction to the causes of mental health problems.

Romme, M. & Escher, S. (2011). *Psychosis as a personal crisis: An experience-based approach.* London: Routledge.
> Marius Romme and Sandra Escher outline their popular approach and describe the development of the hearing voices movement.

Romme, M. & Escher, S. (2000). *Making sense of voices: A guide for mental health professionals Working with Voice-Hearers.* London: MIND.
> This book combines examples with guidance on how professionals can help voice-hearers to deal with their voices and lead an active and fulfilling life.

Slade, M. (2013). *100 Ways to support recovery. A guide for mental health professionals* (2nd edn.). London: Rethink Mental Illness. Downloadable via www.rethink.org/about-us/commissioning-us/100-ways-to-support-recovery.
> This short text suggests 100 ways in which those working in the mental health sector can aid the recovery of psychiatric patients.

Slade, M. (2009). *Personal recovery and mental illness: a guide for mental health professionals.* Cambridge: Cambridge University Press.
> This book proposes a new conceptual basis for mental health services – the Personal Recovery Framework – which gives primacy to the person rather than the illness, and gives case studies from around the world of approaches to supporting recovery.

Silverstein, S., Moghaddam, B. & Wykes, T. (2013). Schizophrenia: Evolution and synthesis. Camridge, MA: MIT Press.
> 'In this book, leading researchers consider conceptual and technical obstacles to progress in understanding schizophrenia and suggest novel strategies for advancing research and treatment.'

Tew, J. (2011). *Social approaches to mental distress.* Basingstoke: Palgrave Macmillan.
This book offers a holistic model for understanding and responding to mental distress. It places mental health within its broader social context, encouraging engagement with not just the person experiencing mental distress, but also their family and wider social world.

Williams, P. (2012). Rethinking psychosis: Towards a paradigm shift in our understanding of psychosis. San Francisco, CA: Sky's Edge Publishing.
'In this eye-opening book, Paris Williams effectively challenges the prevailing myths about the origins and treatment of psychosis, suggesting that it is a natural, although precarious process of self-restoration that should be protected, rather than a hopeless lifelong degenerative brain disease to be managed and medicated.'

Books on the relationship between life circumstances and psychosis

These books describe how our life circumstances (for example our wealth or lack of it, where we live, or whether we are members of a minority group that experiences discrimination) can come together to make it more or less likely that we experience psychosis.

'Race' and ethnicity

Clifford, T. (1984). *Tibetan buddhist medicine and psychiatry: The diamond healing.* Maine, USA: Samuel Weiser.
This introduces to the reader the traditional Tibetan art of healing. It outlines its religious, philosophical and psychological foundations, its history and deities, and its particular methods of diagnosis and treatment.

Fernando, S. (2010). *Mental health, race and culture* (3rd edn). Basingstoke: MacMillan.
A good overview from a social psychiatrist about the role of racism in the development of mental health problems, in the mental health industry and in wider society.

Jackson, V. (2001). *In our own voice: African-American stories of oppression, survival and recovery in mental health systems.* Massachusetts: National Empowerment Center.

Littlewood, R. & Lipsedge, M. (1997). *Aliens and alienists: Ethnic minorities and psychiatry* (3rd edn). London: Routledge.
Two psychiatrists (one trained in medical anthropology) examine their profession's attitudes and actions towards service users from black and minority ethnic communities.

Metzl, J. (2009). *The protest psychosis: How schizophrenia became a black disease.* Boston: Beacon Press.
This is an exploration of how non-conformity is more likely to be seen as 'psychosis' if the person concerned is black. Psychiatrist Jonathan Metzl also explores the more general question of whether what we see as psychosis is sometimes better understood as social non-conformity.

Sutherland, P., Moodley, P. & Chevannes, B. (2014). *Caribbean healing traditions. Implications for health and mental health.* London & New York: Routledge.
This book examines traditional forms of healing, contrasting them with what it sees as the Western cultural imperialism of the current 'global mental health' approach

Poverty/Social Class

Mirowsky, J. & Ross, C.E. (2003). *Social causes of psychological distress.* New Brunswick: Aldine.
A good summary of the evidence that the events and circumstances of our lives affect our mental health.

Warner, R. (1985). *Recovery from schizophrenia: Psychiatry and political economy.* London: Routledge.
A careful study by social psychiatrist Richard Warner of how rates of recovery from psychosis are affected by economic conditions.

Wilkinson, R. & Pickett, K. (2010). *The spirit level: Why equality is better for everyone.* London: Penguin.
This book summarises evidence suggesting that beyond a certain average income level, inequality is more important than absolute wealth in determining rates of mental health problems in a particular country. Rates are higher in unequal countries – those with larger gaps in income between rich and poor, such as the UK – than countries that are more equitable, for example Norway.

Gender

Brown, G. & Harris, T. (1978). *The social origins of depression.* London; Tavistock.
The first major study of a large group of ordinary women and the life events and circumstances that appeared to increase risk of depression.

Busfield, J. (1996). *Men, women and madness: Understanding gender and mental disorder.* London: Macmillan.
An overview from a medical sociologist who takes a critical look at the evidence linking gender and mental health.

Kalathil, J, Collier, B. Bhakta, R., Daniel, O. Joseph, D. & Trivedi, P. (2011). *Recovery and resilience: African, African Caribbean and South Asian women's narratives of recovering from mental distress.* London: Mental Health Foundation and Survivor Research.
An analysis of interviews with women from BME communities about their experience of mental health problems and what helps.

Patel, V. (2001). Poverty, inequality and mental health in developing countries. In D. Leon & G. Walt (Eds.) *Poverty, inequality and health.* Oxford: Oxford University Press.
This book chapter outlines the links between poverty and inequality in developing countries and the risk of mental health problems.

Pilgrim, D. (2014). *Understanding mental health: A critical realist exploration.* London: Routledge.
This book discusses the various aspects of our lives that can contribute to mental health problems: as our biological and psychological makeup, and the events and circumstances of our lives. It also explores the way these can interact in different ways for different people.

Rogers, A. & Pilgrim, D. (2014). *A sociology of mental health and illness.* Buckingham: Open University Press.
An extensive overview of how the circumstances of our lives affect our mental health. It covers race, age, gender and social class.

Rogers, A. & Pilgrim, D. (2003). *Mental health and inequality.* Basingstoke: Palgrave.
An overview of the social sources of mental health problems and the ways in which services treat some groups differently to others.

Ussher, J. (1991). *Women's madness: Misogyny or mental illness?* London: Harvester Wheatsheaf.
A feminist critique of how mainstream mental health services understand and treat women's psychological distress. How various life circumstances can come together and interact (sometimes called 'intersectionality').

Books about how people in different cultures and parts of the world approach mental health

Bhawuk, D. (2011). *Spirituality and Indian psychology: Lessons from the Bhagavad-Gita.* New York: Springer Science & Business Media
An introduction to Indian psychology and spirituality.

Clifford, T. (1984). *Tibetan Buddhist medicine and psychiatry: The diamond healing.* Main, USA: Samuel Weiser.
An introduction to the Tibetan approach to health and mental health.

Halliburton, M. (2009). *Mudpacks and Prozac. Experiencing ayurvedic, biomedical and religious healing.* Walnut Creek, California: Left Coast Press.
An investigation into the different ways in which Ayurvedic, Western, and religious (Christian, Muslim, and Hindu) healing systems approach mental health.

Hammer, L. (1990). *Dragon Rises, Red Bird Flies: Psychology & Chinese Medicine.* New York: Station Hill Press.
A Westerner investigates traditional Chines healing arts such as acupuncture and herbalism.

Hobart, A. (2003). *Healing performances of Bali: Between darkness and light.* New York & Oxford: Berghahn Books
An anthropologist from the UK investigates the Balinese approach to health and mental health.

Kakar, S. (1984). *Shamans, Mystics and Doctors. A psychological inquiry into India and its healing tradition.* London: Unwin Paperbacks.
A psychoanalyst investigates the healing traditions of India.

Kleinman, A. (1988). *Rethinking psychiatry: From cultural category to personal experience.* Free Press, New York.
A Harvard psychiatrist and anthropologist examines how people in different cultures and parts of the world approach mental health.

Kim, U., Yang, K.S., & Hwang, K.K. (Eds.) (2006). *Indigenous and cultural psychology: Understanding people in context.* New York: Springer Science & Business Media.
Different approaches to psychology around the world

Littlewood, R. & Lipsedge, M. (1997). *Aliens and alienists: Ethnic minorities and psychiatry* (3rd edn). London: Routledge.
A classic text looking at the links between racism, psychological ill health and inadequate treatment of ethnic minorities.

Metzl, J. (2011). *The protest psychosis how schizophrenia became a black disease.* Boston, MA: Beacon Press

Taking one hospital as an example, psychiatrist Jonathan Metzl examines how the term 'schizophrenia' changed its meaning over time, and came to be applied disproportionately to young black men who protest. He also documents how anxieties about race continue to impact on relationships between professionals and service users.

Mills, C. (2013). *Decolonizing global mental health the psychiatrization of the majority world.* London & New York: Routledge.

Psychologist China Mills examines and critiques the 'Global Mental Health' movement, arguing that Western approaches to mental health are not always helpful in other parts of the world, and that introducing them can be a form of colonialism.

Moodley, R. & West, W. (2005). *Integrating traditional healing practices into counselling and psychotherapy.* Thousand Oaks, London & New Delhi: Sage

Explores the complexities of using ideas and practices from different traditions within counselling and psychotherapy.

Roopnarine, J.L., & Chadee, D.E. (2016). *Caribbean psychology: Indigenous contributions to a global discipline.* Washington D.C.: American Psychological Association.

This book argues that researchers, practitioners, and organisations must collaborate to create a unified Caribbean psychology that meets the needs of people of Caribbean origin living both in the region and around the world.

Sax, W.S. (2009). *God of justice: Ritual healing and social justice in the central Himalayas.* Oxford: Oxford University Press.

Describes a Himalayan approach to healing.

Stastny, P. & Lehmann, P. (Eds) (2007). *Alternatives beyond psychiatry.* Berlin: Peter Lehmann Publishing.

Sixty-one authors from around the world, including both professionals and service users address questions such as 'What helps me if I go mad?', 'How can I find trustworthy help for a friend or relative?' and 'How can I protect myself from coercive treatment?'.

Sutherland, P., Moodley, R. & Chevannes, B. (2014). *Caribbean healing traditions: Implications for health and mental health.* New York and London: Routledge.

Explains how professionals can provide appropriate care for people of Caribbean heritage.

Tseng, W.S., Chang, S.C., & Nishizono, M. (Eds) (2005). *Asian culture and psychotherapy: Implications for East and West.* Honolulu: University of Hawaii Press.

A useful book for clinicians working with people from an Asian background.

Student textbooks

Cromby, J., Harper, D. & Reavey, P. (2013). *Psychology, mental health and distress.* Basingstoke: Palgrave Macmillan.
This is the first mainstream textbook to take a consistently psychological approach to problems – such as low mood and hearing voices – that psychology courses have sometimes called 'abnormal psychology' and addressed within a psychiatric diagnostic framework. It provides a fully rounded account of mental distress, including social and relationship causes and is now a set text on many psychology, nursing, occupational therapy and social work courses.

Self-help books

Escher, S. & Romme, M. (2010). *Children hearing voices: What you need to know and what you can do.* Ross-on-Wye: PCCS Books.
This book provides aims to provide support and practical solutions for the experience of hearing voices. It is in two parts, one part for children who hear voices, and the other part for parents and adult carers.

Fadden, G., James, C. & Pinfold, V. (2012). *Caring for yourself – Self help for families and friends supporting people with mental health problems.* Birmingham: White Halo Design.
A downloadable workbook. 'Rethink Mental Illness and the Meriden Family Programme have created *Caring for yourself* to help people with mental health problems and carers, family and friends. It is for you if you support someone with any mental health condition. You may have a relative struggling with anxiety, depression or bipolar disorder, a friend with psychosis, schizophrenia or a personality disorder. Whatever the diagnosis, *Caring for yourself* can help you to develop skills and new ways to cope.'

Freeman, D. & Freeman, J. (2008). *Paranoia: The 21st century fear.* Oxford: Oxford University Press.
Daniel Freeman is a leading researcher on paranoia and one of the contributors to this report. Together with his brother Jason Freeman, in this book he analyses the causes of paranoia, identifying the social and cultural factors that seem to be skewing the way we think and feel about the world around us. They explain why paranoia may be on the rise and what we can do to tackle it.

Freeman, D., Freeman, J. & Garety, P. (2006). *Overcoming paranoid and suspicious thoughts: A self-help guide using cognitive behavioral techniques.* London: Constable & Robinson.
Research suggests that 20–30 per cent of people in the UK frequently have suspicious or paranoid thoughts. This is a practical self-help guide written by two of the foremost researchers in the field, both contributors to this report.

Hayward, M., Strauss, C. & Kingdon, D. (2012). *Overcoming distressing voices.* London: Constable & Robinson.
A self-help guide based on a cognitive behavioural approach.

Holford, P. (2007). *Optimum nutrition for the mind.* London: Piatkus Books.
Patrick Holford suggests how good nutrition can help with mental health problems.

Moncrieff, J. (2009). *A straight talking introduction to psychiatric drugs.* Ross-on-Wye: PCCS Books.
> A book which aims to give service users the information they need to make informed choices about psychiatric drugs. It contains practical advice on the best questions to ask if you are prescribed medication for mental health problems, and what is likely to happen if you come off or cut down.

Morrison, A., Renton, J., French, P. & Bentall, R. (2008). *Think you're crazy? Think again: A resource book for cognitive therapy for psychosis.* London: Routledge.
> A self-help book based on a cognitive-behavioural approach and written by respected researchers in the field.

Romme, M. & Escher, S. (2003). *Accepting voices.* London: MIND Publications.
> The book illustrates that many people hear voices and that not everyone has recourse to psychiatry, but that there are ways of coping which enable people to come to terms with their experience. It focuses on techniques to deal with voices, emphasising that personal growth should be stimulated rather than inhibited.

Turkington, D., Kingdon, D., Rathod, S., Wilcock, S., Brabban, A., Cromarty, P., Dudley, R., Gray, R., Pelton, J., Siddle, R. & Weiden, P. (2009). *Back to life, back to normality: Cognitive therapy, recovery and psychosis.* Cambridge: Cambridge University Press.
> A guide for people experiencing psychosis, their families and friends. Based on a cognitive behavioural approach.

Self-help organisations and the service user/survivor movement

Chamberlin, J. (1988, Kindle edn. 2012). *On our own: Patient controlled alternatives to the mental health system.* London: Mind Publishing. Chapter 5 available free via http://home.earthlink.net/~allan.hunter/psych_inmates_libfront/vol_4/Chamberlin/Chamberlin_Ch5.html.
> Judi Chamberlin was one of the pioneers of the survivor movement in mental health. Her book makes a compelling case for 'patient-controlled services' – viable and more humane alternatives to the institutions that she feels destroy the confident independence of so many people.

James, A. (2001). *Raising our voices: An account of the Hearing Voices movement.* Gloucester: Handsell.
> Adam James tells the story of the hearing voices movement which has revolutionised how we think about the experience, and led to the formation of hundreds of self-help groups for people who hear voices.

The psychiatric drugs debate

Moncrieff, J. (2013). *The bitterest pills: the troubling story of antipsychotic drugs.* London: Palgrave Macmillan.

Psychiatrist Joanna Moncrieff challenges the conventional view that antipsychotics are specific treatments which target an underlying brain disease. She suggests that professionals have often exaggerated the benefits of antipsychotics and minimised or ignored evidence of their toxic effects, and that the pharmaceutical industry has been involved in expanding their use into territory where it is likely that their dangers far outweigh their advantages.

Moncrieff, J. (2009). *The myth of the chemical cure: A critique of psychiatric drug treatment.* London: Palgrave Macmillan.

This book examines research on antipsychotics, antidepressants, mood stabilisers and stimulants. It suggests that psychiatric drugs work by creating altered mental states, which suppress not only 'symptoms' but also other intellectual and emotional functions. Joanna Moncrieff discusses the pros and cons of different sorts of drugs and suggests that acknowledging the real nature of psychiatric drugs would lead to a more democratic practice of psychiatry.

Read, J. (2009). *Psychiatric drugs: key issues and service user perspectives.* London: Palgrave Macmillan.

This lively and provocative overview examines the lived experience of taking psychiatric drugs. The book examines the consequences of long-term psychiatric drug use from the perspectives of people who have taken them and tried coming off them. It draws out possible tensions between patients and professionals about medication and offers examples of how to resolve these constructively.

Whitaker, R. (2011). *Anatomy of an epidemic: Magic bullets, psychiatric drugs, and the astonishing rise of mental illness in America.* New York: Broadway Books.

Award-winning science and history writer Robert Whitaker investigates why the number of those classified as 'disabled mentally ill' in the United States has tripled over the past two decades. He examines evidence that psychiatric drugs can do harm if taken long-term.

The mental health system and society's approach to 'mental illness'

Bentall, R. (2010). *Doctoring the mind: Why psychiatric treatments fail.* London: Penguin Books.
Why is the Western world's treatment of mental illness so flawed? Who really benefits from psychiatry? And why would a patient in Nigeria have a much greater chance of recovery than one in the UK?

Coles, S., Keenan, S. & Diamond, R. (2013). *Madness contested. Power and practice.* Ross-on-Rye: PCCS Books.
Twenty-one chapters critically analyse the dominance of medical approaches to madness and discuss alternatives in theory and practice.

Kinderman, P. (2014). *A prescription for psychiatry: A manifesto for a radical vision of mental health and wellbeing.* Basingstoke: Palgrave.
'*A prescription for psychiatry* lays bare the flaws and failings of traditional mental health care and offers a radical alternative. Exposing the old-fashioned biological "disease model" of psychiatry as unscientific and unhelpful, it calls for a revolution in the way we plan and deliver care. Kinderman challenges the way we think about mental health problems, arguing that the origins of distress are largely social, and urges a change from a 'disease model' to a "psychosocial model". The book persuasively argues that we should significantly reduce our use of psychiatric medication, and help should be tailored to each person's unique needs. This is a manifesto for an entirely new approach to psychiatric care; one that truly offers care rather than coercion, therapy rather than medication, and a return to the common sense appreciation that distress is usually an understandable reaction to life's challenges.'

Laurance, J. (2002). *Pure madness: How fear drives the mental health system.* London: Routledge.
The then Health Editor of *The Independent* travels round the UK talking to staff and service users in mental health services. He finds a service driven by fear.

Rapley, M., Moncrieff, J. & Dillon, J. (2011). *De-medicalizing misery: Psychiatry, psychology and the human condition.* Basingstoke: Palgrave Macmillan.
The book argues that human experience is increasingly being pathologised and 'psychiatrised' and that 'mental health problems' are essentially moral and political, rather than medical matters.

Sue, D.W. & Sue, D. (2012). *Counseling the culturally diverse: Theory and practice.* New Jersey: Wiley.
The most widely used and acclaimed text on multicultural counselling.

Tummey, R. & Turner, T. (2008). *Critical issues in mental health.* Basingstoke: Palgrave McMillan.
'Knowledgeable writers … confront us with all the major issues that must be addressed in order to create more humane and effective mental health services.'

Watters, E. (2011). *Crazy like us.* London: Robinson Publishing.
Ethan Watters suggests that over the last decades, mental illnesses popularised in America have been spreading across the globe with the speed of contagious diseases. He travels around the world and reaches the conclusion that the virus is the US – American culture constantly shapes and sometimes creates the mental illnesses of our time. Watters suggests that by setting aside its role as the world's therapist, the US may come to accept that it has as much to learn from other cultures' beliefs about the mind as it has to teach.

Whitaker, R. (2010). *Mad in America: Bad science, bad medicine and the enduring mistreatment of the mentally ill.* New York: Basic Books.

'Tracing over three centuries of "cures" for madness, Robert Whitaker suggests that medical therapies – from "spinning" or "chilling" patients in colonial times to more modern methods of electroshock, lobotomy, and drugs – have been used to silence patients and dull their minds, deepening their suffering and impairing their hope of recovery'. Whitaker presents evidence that people diagnosed with schizophrenia in the United States fare worse than those in poor countries, and possibly worse than asylum patients did in the early nineteenth century. He argues that modern psychiatric drugs are just old medicine in new bottles and that we as a society are deluded about their efficacy.

Details of Contributors

About the Editor

Anne Cooke is a consultant clinical psychologist who worked in the NHS for many years with people distressed by the types of experiences that are the subject of this report. She is now Principal Lecturer and Clinical Director of the Doctoral Programme in Clinical Psychology at the Salomons Centre for Applied Psychology, Canterbury Christ Church University. With Professor Peter Kinderman, she was also co-ordinating editor of the report *Recent Advances in Understanding Mental Illness and Psychotic Experiences* which this one updates and replaces, published in 2000. She was a co-editor of *Understanding Bipolar Disorder*, a Division of Clinical Psychology report published in 2010. She is active on Twitter (@AnneCooke14) and blogs at *Discursive of Tunbridge Wells*.

About the contributors

Thurstine Basset (@ThurstineBasset) is Director, Basset Consultancy and first author of *Psychosis Revisited*.

Richard Bentall (@RichardBentall) is Professor of Clinical Psychology, University of Liverpool.

Mary Boyle is Emeritus Professor of Clinical Psychology, University of East London.

Anne Cooke (@AnneCooke14) is Principal Lecturer and Clinical Director of the Doctoral Programme in Clinical Psychology, Canterbury Christ Church University.

Caroline Cupitt is Consultant Clinical Psychologist, South London and Maudsley NHS Trust.

Jacqui Dillon (@JacquiDillon) is a writer, campaigner, international speaker and trainer.

Daniel Freeman (@ProfDFreeman) is Professor of Clinical Psychology, University of Oxford.

Philippa Garety is Professor of Clinical Psychology, King's College London Institute of Psychiatry, Psychology and Neuroscience, and Clinical Director and Joint Leader of the Psychosis Clinical Academic Group, South London and Maudsley NHS Foundation Trust, King's Health Partners..

David Harper is Reader in Clinical Psychology, University of East London.

Lucy Johnstone (@ClinpsychLucy) is Consultant Clinical Psychologist and independent trainer.

Peter Kinderman (@peterkinderman) is Professor of Clinical Psychology at the University of Liverpool.

Elizabeth Kuipers is Professor Emerita of Clinical Psychology, King's College London Institute of Psychiatry, Psychology and Neuroscience.

Tony Lavender is Pro Vice-Chancellor and Professor of Clinical Psychology, Canterbury Christ Church University.

Laura Lea is Coordinator of Service User and Carer Involvement, Salomons Centre for Applied Psychology, Canterbury Christ Church University.

Eleanor Longden is Research Psychologist, University of Manchester and Greater Manchester West Mental Health Trust.

Rufus May (@Rufusmay) is Clinical Psychologist, Greater Manchester West Mental Health Trust.

Sara Meddings is Consultant Clinical Psychologist, Sussex Partnership NHS Trust.

Tony Morrison is Professor of Clinical Psychology, University of Manchester.

Steve Onyett was Associate Professor, University of Exeter and Director, Onyett Entero Ltd. Very sadly, he passed away in September 2015. We are hugely grateful for his passionate contribution to this project, and his warm encouragement throughout the editorial process.

Emmanuelle Peters s Reader in Clinical Psychology, King's College London Institute of Psychiatry, Psychology and Neuroscience.

David Pilgrim is Professor of Health and Social Policy, University of Liverpool.

John Read (@ReadReadj) is Professor of Clinical Psychology and Director of the Doctorate of Clinical Psychology Programme, University of East London.

Mike Slade is Mental Health Recovery and Social Inclusion, University of Nottingham.

Dame Til Wykes is Professor of Clinical Psychology, King's College London Institute of Psychiatry, Psychology and Neuroscience.

Yan Weaver is Development Worker, Voice Collective, London.

References

References have been chosen to illustrate and evidence the points made in this report: they are not comprehensive. On points of debate, references illustrate the different points of view.

Acknowledgement

1. Kalathil, J. & Faulkner, A. (2015). Racialisation and knowledge production: A critique of the report Understanding Psychosis and Schizophrenia. *Mental Health Today*, Jan-Feb 2015, 22-23.

Foreword

1. Jones, S., Lobban, F. & Cooke, A. (2010). *Understanding bipolar disorder: Why some people experience extreme mood states and what can help.* Division of Clinical Psychology. Leicester: The British Psychological Society. Available from www.bpsshop.org.uk/Understanding-Bipolar-Disorder-P1280.aspx

Executive Summary

1. Jones, S., Lobban, F. & Cooke, A. (2010). *Understanding bipolar disorder: Why some people experience extreme mood states and what can help.* Division of Clinical Psychology. Leicester: The British Psychological Society. Available from www.bpsshop.org.uk/ Understanding-Bipolar-Disorder-P1280.aspx

2. British Psychological Society Division of Clinical Psychology (in preparation). *Understanding 'depression': Why people experience persistent low mood and what can help.* Leicester, BPS. www.understandingdepression.net

Part 1

Section 1

1. Jones, S., Lobban, F. & Cooke, A. (2010). *Understanding bipolar disorder: Why some people experience extreme mood states and what can help.* Division of Clinical Psychology. Leicester: The British Psychological Society. Available from www.bpsshop.org.uk/Understanding-Bipolar-Disorder-P1280.aspx

2. British Psychological Society Division of Clinical Psychology (in preparation). *Understanding 'depression': Why people experience persistent low mood and what can help.* Leicester, BPS. www.understandingdepression.net

3. Jones, S., Lobban, F. & Cooke, A. (2010). *Understanding bipolar disorder: Why some people experience extreme mood states and what can help.* Division of Clinical Psychology. Leicester: The British Psychological Society. Available from www.bpsshop.org.uk/Understanding-Bipolar-Disorder-P1280.aspx

4. Goldberg, T.E., Aloia, M., Gourovitch, M.C., Missar, D., Pickar, D. & Weinberger, D.R. (1998). Cognitive substrates of thought disorder, I: The semantic system. *American Journal of Psychiatry, 155*, 1671–1676. http://journals.psychiatryonline.org/data/Journals/AJP/3695/1671.pdf

5.   Rachel. (2013). *Experiences of psychosis: First episode of psychosis.* Retrieved 17 January 2014 from http://healthtalkonline.org/content/rachel-interview-14-1

6.   Graham. (2013). Experiences of psychosis: First episode of psychosis. Retrieved 17 January 2014 from http://healthtalkonline.org/content/graham-interview-27

7.   Kalathil, J. (2011). Recovery and Resilience: African, African-Caribbean and South Asian women's narratives of recovering from mental distress. Retrieved 1 December 2016 from www.mentalhealth.org.uk/publications/recovery-and-resilience/

8.   May, R. (2013). Retrieved 24 October 24 2013 from www.rufusmay.com/

9.   Miriam. (2012). Personal accounts of paranoia. Retrieved 17 January 2014 from Paranoid Thoughts: www.paranoidthoughts.com/accounts.php

10.   Gelder, M., Gath, D. & Mayou, R. (1983). *Oxford textbook of psychiatry.* Oxford: Oxford University Press.

11.   May, R. (2013). Retrieved 24 October 24 2013 from www.rufusmay.com/

12.   Miriam. (2012). Personal accounts of paranoia. Retrieved 17 January 2014, from www.paranoidthoughts.com/accounts.php

13.   Mary. In Jackson, L., Hayward, M. & Cooke, A. (2011). Developing positive relationships with voices: A preliminary grounded theory. *International Journal of Social Psychiatry, 57*(5), 487–495: http://isp.sagepub.com/content/early/2010/06/30/0020764010368624.full.pdf

14.   Bidois, E. (2012). A cultural and personal perspective of psychosis. In J. Geekie, P. Randal, D. Lampshire, & J. Read (Eds.), *Experiencing psychosis: Personal and professional perspectives* (pp.35-43). London: Routledge.

15.   Fernando, S. (2000). Imperialism, racism and psychiatry. In P. Barker & C. Stevenson (Eds.), *Construction of Power and Authority in Psychiatry.* (pp.81-95). Heinemann: Oxford.

16.   Pilgrim, D. (2008). The eugenics legacy in psychology and psychiatry. *Experiencing psychosis: Personal and professional perspectives 54*(3), 272–284.

17.   American Psychological Association (1993). Guidelines for providers of psychological services to ethnic, linguistic and culturally diverse populations. *American Psychologist, 48,* 45-48.

18.   Grier, W. & Cobbs, P. (1969). *Black Rage.* New York: Bantam Books.

19.   Karlsen, S. (2005). Racism, psychosis and common mental disorder among ethnic minority groups in England. *Psychological Medicine, 35*(12), 1795-1803.
      doi: 10.1017/S0033291705005830

Section 2

1.   British Psychological Society (2000). *Recent advances in understanding mental illness and psychotic experiences.* Division of Clinical Psychology. Leicester: British Psychological Society. www.schizophrenia.com/research/Rep03.pdf

2.   Bentall, R.P. (2003). *Madness explained: Psychosis and human nature.* London: Penguin Books.

3.   Van Os, J., Hansen, M., Bijl, R. & Ravelli, A. (2000). Strauss (1969) revisited: Evidence for a psychosis continuum in the general population? *Schizophrenia Research, 45*(1–2), 11-20. http://www.sciencedirect.com/science/article/pii/S0920996499002248

4. Johns, L.C., Kompus, K., Connell, M., Humpston, C., Lincoln, T.M., Longden, E. et al. (2014). Auditory verbal hallucinations in persons with and without a need for care. *Schizophrenia Bulletin, 40*(4), S255–S264.
http://schizophreniabulletin.oxfordjournals.org/content/40/Suppl_4/S255.full.pdf+html

5. Schizophrenia Commission (2012). *The abandoned illness: A report from the Schizophrenia Commission.* London: Rethink Mental Illness.
www.rethink.org/media/514093/TSC_main_report_14_nov.pdf

6. Beavan, V., Read, J. & Cartwright, C. (2011). The prevalence of voice-hearers in the general population: a literature review. *Journal of Mental Health, 20*(3), 281–292.
http://informahealthcare.com/doi/pdf/10.3109/09638237.2011.562262

7. Van Os, J., Kenis, G. & Rutten, B.P. (2010). The environment and schizophrenia. *Nature, 468*(7321), 203–212. www.ncbi.nlm.nih.gov/pubmed/21068828

8. Freeman, D., Garety, P.A., Bebbington, P.E., Smith, B., Rollinson, R., Fowler, D. et al. (2005). Psychological investigation of the structure of paranoia in a non-clinical population. *British Journal of Psychiatry, 186*, 427–435.
www.nelft.nhs.uk/_documentbank/Paranoia_paper_2005.pdf

9. Karen. (2012). Voices and positive feelings. In M. Hayward, C. Strauss, & D. Kingdon (Eds.), *Overcoming distressing voices: A self-help guide using cognitive behavioral techniques.* London: Constable & Robinson.

10. Romme, M. & Escher, S. (1993). *Accepting voices.* London: MIND Publications.

11. Romme, M., & Escher, S. (1993). *Accepting voices.* London: MIND Publications.

Section 3

1. Andrew, E., Gray, N.S. & Snowden, R.J. (2008). The relationship between trauma and beliefs about hearing voices: A study of psychiatric and non-psychiatric voice hearers. *Psychological Medicine, 38*(10), 1409-1417.
http://psych.cf.ac.uk/home2/snowden/2008_PsychMed_Andrews%20etal.pdf

2. Bentall, R.P. (2003). *Madness explained: psychosis and human nature.* London: Penguin Books.

3. Freeman, D., Garety, P.A., Bebbington, P.E., Smith, B., Rollinson, R., Fowler, D. et al. (2005). Psychological investigation of the structure of paranoia in a non-clinical population. *British Journal of Psychiatry, 186*, 427–435.
www.nelft.nhs.uk/_documentbank/Paranoia_paper_2005.pdf

4. Adam. (2010). Experiencing suspicious thoughts and paranoia: An account. *Schizophrenia Bulletin, 37*(4), 656–658.
www.ncbi.nlm.nih.gov/pmc/articles/PMC3122296/pdf/sbq123.pdf

5. Romme, M., Escher, S., Dillon, J., Corstens, D. & Morris, M. (2009). *Living with Voices: 50 Stories of Recovery.* Ross-on-Wye: PCCS.

6. Amber. (2012). *Personal accounts of paranoia.* Retrieved 17 January 2014 from Paranoid Thoughts: www.paranoidthoughts.com/accounts.php

7. Beavan, V., Read, J. & Cartwright, C. (2011). The prevalence of voice-hearers in the general population: a literature review. *Journal of Mental Health, 20*(3), 281–292. http://informahealthcare.com/doi/pdf/10.3109/09638237.2011.562262

8. Bebbington, P.E., McBride, O., Steel, C., Kuipers, E., Radovanovic, M., Brugha, T. et al. (2013). The structure of paranoia in the general population. *British Journal of Psychiatry, 202*, 419–427. http://bjp.rcpsych.org/content/202/6/419.full.pdf+html

9. Van Os, J., Linscott, R.J., Myin-Germeys, I., Delespaul, P. & Krabbendam, L. (2009). A systematic review and meta-analysis of the psychosis continuum: evidence for a psychosis proneness-persistence-impairment model of psychotic disorder. *Psychological Medicine, 39*(2), 179–195. http://journals.cambridge.org/action/displayAbstract?fromPage=online&aid=3405404

10. Hemsley, D.R. (1993). A simple (or simplistic?) cognitive model of schizophrenia. *Behaviour Research and Therapy, 31*, 633–646. www.sciencedirect.com/science/article/pii/000579679390116C

11. Jackson, L., Hayward, M. & Cooke, A. (2011). Developing positive relationships with voices: A preliminary grounded theory. *International Journal of Social Psychiatry, 57*(5), 487–495. http://isp.sagepub.com/content/57/5/487.long

12. Clarke, I. (2010). *Psychosis and spirituality: Consolidating the new paradigm* (2nd edn.). London: Wiley Blackwell.

13. Heriot-Maitland, C., Knight, M. & Peters, E. (2012). A qualitative comparison of psychotic-like phenomena in clinical and non-clinical populations. *British Journal of Clinical Psychology, 51*(1), 37–53. www.ncbi.nlm.nih.gov/pubmed/22268540

14. Romme, M. & Escher, S. (1993). *Accepting voices.* London: MIND Publications.

15. Bhugra, D. (1996). *Psychiatry and religion.* London: Routledge.

16. The Icarus Project (2013). *The Icarus Project: Navigating the space between brilliance and madness.* Retrieved 11 November 2013 from www.theicarusproject.net

17. American Psychiatric Association (2013). *Diagnostic and statistical manual of mental disorders* (fifth edn.). Arlington, VA: American Psychiatric Association Publishing.

18. Hacking, I. (2013, August 8). Lost in the forest. (M. Wilmers, Ed.) *London Review of Books, 35*(15), 7–8. www.lrb.co.uk/v35/n15/ian-hacking/lost-in-the-forest

19. Kirk, S. & Kutchins, H. (1994). The myth of the reliability of the DSM. *Journal of Mind and Behaviour, 15*, 71–86. www.academyanalyticarts.org/kirk&kutchins.htm

20. Van Os, J., Gilvarry, C., Bale, R., Van Horn, E., Tattan, T., White, I. et al. (1999). A comparison of the utility of dimensional and categorical representations of psychosis. *Psychological Medicine, 29*(3), 595–606. www.ncbi.nlm.nih.gov/pubmed/10405080

21. Griffiths, R. (nd). *Inquiry into the 'schizophrenia' label.* Retrieved 21 May 2014, from www.schizophreniainquiry.org

22. Mill, J.S. (2014, January 17). *John Stuart Mill.* Retrieved 22 January 2014 from www.en.wikiquote.org/wiki/John_Stuart_Mill

23. Van Os, J., Linscott, R.J., Myin-Germeys, I., Delespaul, P. & Krabbendam, L. (2009). A systematic review and meta-analysis of the psychosis continuum: evidence for a psychosis proneness-persistence-impairment model of psychotic disorder. *Psychological Medicine, 39*(2), 179–195. http://dare.ubvu.vu.nl/bitstream/handle/1871/23548/239125.pdf?sequence=1

24. Insel, T. (2013, April 29). *Directors blog: Transforming diagnosis.* Retrieved 11 January 2014 from www.nimh.nih.gov/about/director/2013/transforming-diagnosis.shtml

25. American Psychiatric Association (2013). *Diagnostic and statistical manual of mental disorders* (fifth edn.). Arlington, VA: American Psychiatric Association Publishing.

26. Campbell, J.K., O'Rourke, M. & Slater, M. (2011). *Carving nature at its joints: Natural kinds in metaphysics and science.* Cambridge, MA: MIT Press.

27. Beavan, V., Read, J. & Cartwright, C. (2011). The prevalence of voice-hearers in the general population: a literature review. *Journal of Mental Health, 20*(3), 281–292. http://informahealthcare.com/doi/pdf/10.3109/09638237.2011.562262

28. National Institute of Mental Health (2013). *Research domain criteria (RDoC).* Retrieved 2 January 2014 from www.nimh.nih.gov/research-priorities/rdoc/index.shtml?utm_source=govdelivery&utm_medium=email&utm_campaign=govdelivery

29. Collins, N. (2010, July 28). *Eccentrics 'could be diagnosed with mental disorders'.* Retrieved 14 November 2013 from www.telegraph.co.uk/health/healthnews/7913122/Eccentrics-could-be-diagnosed-with-mental-disorders.html

30. Schwartz, R.C. & Blankenship, D.M. (2014). Racial disparities in psychotic disorder diagnosis: A review of empirical literature. *World Journal of Psychiatry 22, 4*(4), 133–140.

31. Neighbors, H.W., Trierweiler, S.J., Briggett C. Ford, B.C. & Muroff, J.R. (2003). Racial differences in DSM diagnosis using a semi-structured instrument: The importance of clinical judgment in the diagnosis of african americans. *Journal of Health and Social Behavior, 44*(3), 237–256. www.jstor.org/stable/1519777?seq=1#page_scan_tab_contents

32. Gara, M.A., Vega, W.A., Arndt, S., Escamilla, M., et. al. (2012). Influence of patient race and ethnicity on clinical assessment in patients with affective disorders. *Archives of General Psychiatry, 69*(6), 593–600. doi:10.1001/archgenpsychiatry.2011.2040

33. Metzl, J.M. (2011). *The Protest Psychosis: How Schizophrenia Became a Black Disease.* Boston, MA: Beacon Press.

34. Pride, F. (2010). Schizophrenia as Political Weapon [Blog post]. The Root. Retrieved 2 December 2016 from www.theroot.com/articles/politics/2010/01/black_men_and_schizophrenia_whats_the_deal/

35. Metzl, J.M. (2011). *The Protest Psychosis: How Schizophrenia Became a Black Disease.* Boston, MA: Beacon Press.

36. Fernando, S. (2015, April). Sanity, Madness and the Family, Family Life: An Urgent Retrospective. Symposium held at the Birkbeck, University of London.

37. Berkson, J. (1950). Are there two regressions? *Journal of the American Statistical Association, 45*(250), 164–180. www.jstor.org/stable/pdfplus/2280676.pdf?acceptTC=true&jpdConfirm=true

38. Maric, N., Myin-Germeys, I., Delespaul, P., de Graaf, R., Vollebergh, W. & Van Os, J. (2004). Is our concept of schizophrenia influenced by Berkson's bias? *Social Psychiatry and Psychiatric Epidemiology, 39*(8), 600–605. www.ncbi.nlm.nih.gov/pubmed/15300369

39. Vázquez-Barquero, J.L., Lastra, I., Cuesta Nuñez, M.J., Herrera Castanedo, S. & Dunn, G. (1996). Patterns of positive and negative symptoms in first episode schizophrenia. *British Journal of Psychiatry, 168*(6), 693–701. www.researchgate.net/publication/14428625_Patterns_of_positive_and_negative_symptoms_in_first_episode_schizophrenia

40. Maric, N., Myin-Germeys, I., Delespaul, P., de Graaf, R., Vollebergh, W. & Van Os, J. (2004). Is our concept of schizophrenia influenced by Berkson's bias? *Social Psychiatry and Psychiatric Epidemiology, 39*(8), 600–605. www.ncbi.nlm.nih.gov/pubmed/15300369

41. Ronald, A., Sieradzka, D., Cardno, A.G., Haworth, C.M., McGuire, P. & Freeman, D. (2013). Characterization of psychotic experiences in adolescence using the specific psychotic experiences questionnaire: Findings from a study of 5000 16-year-old twins. *Schizophrenia Bulletin, 2013*(Sep). http://schizophreniabulletin.oxfordjournals.org/content/early/2013/09/21/schbul.sbt106.full.pdf+html

42. Cohen, P. & Cohen, J. (1984.) The clinician's illusion. *Archives of General Psychiatry, 41*(12). http://people.uncw.edu/leccil/psy525/cohen%20and%20cohenscan0002.pdf

43. Pitt, E., Kilbride, M., Nothard, S., Welford, M. & Morrison, A.P. (2007). Researching recovery from psychosis: a user-led project. *The Psychiatrist, 31,* 55–60. http://pb.rcpsych.org/content/31/2/55.full.pdf+html

44. Boyle, M. (2013). The persistence of medicalisation: Is the presentation of alternatives part of the problem? In S. Coles, S. Keenan, & B. Diamond (Eds.), *Madness contested: Power and practice.* Ross-on-Wye: PCCS Books.

45. Falk, K. (2010). In British Psychological Society *Understanding Bipolar Disorder: Why some people experience extreme mood states and what can help,* p.32. Leicester: British Psychological Society.

46. Rethink (2010). *Recovery insights: Learning from lived experience.* London: Rethink. www.rethink.org/resources/r/recovery-insights

47. Pitt, E., Kilbride, M., Nothard, S., Welford, M. & Morrison, A.P. (2007). Researching recovery from psychosis: a user-led project. *The Psychiatrist, 31,* 55–60. http://pb.rcpsych.org/content/31/2/55.full.pdf+html

48. Horn, N., Johnstone, L. & Brooke, S. (2007). Some service user perspectives on the diagnosis of borderline personality disorder. *Journal of Mental Health, 16*(2), 255–269. http://informahealthcare.com/doi/pdf/10.1080/09638230601056371

49. Thornicroft, G., Brohan, E., Rose, D., Sartorius, N., Leese, M. & the Indigo Study Group (2009). Global pattern of experienced and anticipated discrimination against people with schizophrenia: a cross-sectional survey. *Lancet, 9661,* 408–415. http://tinyurl.com/n3pc9yh

50. Social Exclusion Unit (2004). *Mental health and social exclusion.* London: Office of the Deputy Prime Minister. www.socialfirmsuk.co.uk/resources/library/mental-health-and-social-exclusion-social-exclusion-unit-report

51. Mehta, S. & Farina, A. (1997). Is being 'sick' really better? The effect of the disease view of mental disorder on stigma. *Journal of Social and Clinical Psychology, 16*, 405–419. http://guilfordjournals.com/doi/pdf/10.1521/jscp.1997.16.4.405

52. Marwaha, S., Johnson, S., Bebbington, P., Stafford, M., Angermeyer, M.C., Brugha, T., Azorin, J.-M., Kilian, R., Hansen, K. & Toumi, M. (2007). Rates and correlates of employment in people with schizophrenia living in the UK, France and Germany. *British Journal of Psychiatry, 191*(1), 30–37. http://bjp.rcpsych.org/content/191/1/30.full

53. Angermeyer, M.C., Holzinger, A., Carta, M.G. & Schomerus, G. (2011). Biogenetic explanations and public acceptance of mental illness: systematic review of population studies. *British Journal of Psychiatry, 199*, 367–372. http://bjp.rcpsych.org/content/199/5/367.full.pdf+html

54. Read, J., Haslam, N., Sayce, L. & Davies, E. (2006). Prejudice and schizophrenia: a review of the 'mental illness is an illness like any other' approach. *Acta Psychiatrica Scandinavica, 114*, 303–318. http://onlinelibrary.wiley.com/doi/10.1111/j.1600-0447.2006.00824.x/pdf

55. Cooke, A. (2008). Problems associated with the use of the concept of mental illness. In T. Stickley & T. Basset (Eds.), *Learning about mental health practice* (pp.329–346). Chichester: John Wiley & Sons Ltd. Available from http://tinyurl.com/mk4qyc5

56. Herman, J. (1997). *Trauma and recovery: The aftermath of violence – from domestic abuse to political terror* (new edn). New York: Basic Books.

57. Campbell, P. (2010). Surviving the system. In T. Basset & T. Stickley (Eds.), *Voices of experience: Narratives of mental health survivors*, p.22. Chichester: Wiley-Blackwell.

58. Deegan, P.E. (1993). Recovering our sense of value after being labelled mentally ill. *Journal of Psychosocial Nursing and Mental Health Services, 31*(4), 7–11. www.ncbi.nlm.nih.gov/pubmed/8487230

59. British Psychological Society. (2010). *Understanding bipolar disorder: Why some people experience extreme mood states and what can help*, p.65. Leicester: British Psychological Society. www.bpsshop.org.uk/Understanding-Bipolar-Disorder-P1280.aspx

60. Oquosa, O. (2012). I managed to get schizophrenia diagnosis changed [Online testimony]. Inquiry into the 'Schizophrenia' Label. Retrieved 5 December 2016 from www.schizophreniainquiry.org/testimonies?page=3

61. Pembroke, L.R. (2012). *Self harm perspectives from personal experience*, p.36. Retrieved from http://kreativeinterventions.com/SelfHarmPerspectivesfromPersonalExperience.pdf

62. Henry. In Barham, P. & Hayward, R. (1995). *Re-locating madness: from the mental patient to the person.* London: Free Association Books.

63. British Psychological Society (2013). *Division of Clinical Psychology position statement on the classification of behaviour and experience in relation to functional psychiatric diagnoses: Time for a paradigm shift.* Leicester: British Psychological Society. http://dcp.bps.org.uk/document-download-area/document-download$.cfm?restart=true&file_uuid=9EF109E9-0FB3-ED4F-DF84-310F745854CB

64. Division of Clinical Psychology (2011). *Good practice guidelines on the use of psychological formulation.* Leicester: British Psychological Society. http://shop.bps.org.uk/good-practice-guidelines-on-the-use-of-psychological-formulation.html

65. Schizophrenia Commission (2012). *The abandoned illness: A report from the Schizophrenia Commission.* London: Rethink Mental Illness. www.rethink.org/media/514093/TSC_main_report_14_nov.pdf

66. Thomas, P., Seebohm, P., Wallcraft, J., Kalathil, J. & Fernando, S. (2013). Personal consequences of the diagnosis of schizophrenia: A preliminary report from the inquiry into the 'schizophrenia' label. *Mental Health and Social Inclusion, 17*(3), 135–139.

67. British Psychological Society (2012). *Response to the American Psychiatric Association: DSM-5 development.* Retrieved 31 October 2013 from www.bps.org.uk/news/british-psychological-still-has-concerns-over-dsm-v

68. American Psychiatric Association (2013). *Diagnostic and statistical manual of mental disorders, Fifth Edition (DSM-5).* American Psychiatric Association. www.dsm5.org/

69. World Health Organization (2010). *ICD-10 Version: 2010.* Retrieved 21 May 21 from www.apps.who.int/classifications/icd10/browse/2010/en

70. Division of Clinical Psychology (2013). *Classification of behaviour and experience in relation to functional psychiatric diagnoses: Time for a paradigm shift.* Leicester: British Psychological Society.

71. DxSummit. (2014). *DxSummit.* Retrieved 21 May 2014 from www.dxsummit.org

72. Division of Clinical Psychology (2011). *Good practice guidelines on the use of psychological formulation.* Leicester: British Psychological Society. http://shop.bps.org.uk/good-practice-guidelines-on-the-use-of-psychological-formulation.html

73. Division of Clinical Psychology (2011). *Good practice guidelines on the use of psychological formulation.* Leicester: British Psychological Society. http://shop.bps.org.uk/good-practice-guidelines-on-the-use-of-psychological-formulation.html

74. Johnstone, L. & Dallos, R. (2013). *Formulation in psychology and psychotherapy.* Hove: Routledge.

Section 4

1. Van Os, J., Linscott, R.J., Myin-Germeys, I., Delespaul, P. & Krabbendam, L. (2009). A systematic review and meta-analysis of the psychosis continuum: evidence for a psychosis proneness-persistence-impairment model of psychotic disorder. *Psychological Medicine, 39*(2), 179–195. http://tinyurl.com/ovt6mll

2. Slade, M., Amering, M. & Oades, L. (2008). Recovery: an international perspective. *Epidemiologia e Psichiatria Sociale, 17*, 128–137. www.ncbi.nlm.nih.gov/pubmed/18589629

3. Whitaker, R. (2002). *Mad in America.* Cambridge, MA: Perseus Publishing.

4. Zipursky, R., Reilly, T. & Murray, R. (2012). The myth of schizophrenia as a progressive brain disease. *Schizophrenia Bulletin, 135.* http://schizophreniabulletin.oxfordjournals.org/content/39/6/1363.full.pdf+html

5. Shepherd, G., Boardman, J. & Slade, M. (2008, March 17). Making recovery a reality. Retrieved 11 November 2013 from Sainsbury Centre for Mental Health: www.centreformentalhealth.org.uk/pdfs/Making_recovery_a_reality_policy_paper.pdf

6. Bebbington, P.E., Wilkins, S., Jones, P., Foerster, A., Murray, R.M., Toone, B. et al. (1993). Life events and psychosis: Initial results from the Camberwell Collaborative Psychosis Study. *British Journal of Psychiatry, 162*, 358–362. http://bjp.rcpsych.org/content/162/1/72.full.pdf

7. May, R. (2000). Routes to recovery from psychosis: The routes of a clinical psychologist. *Clinical Psychology Forum, 146*, 6–10.

8. Stockdale, S.E., Wells, K.B., Tang, L., Belin, T.R., Zhang, L. & Sherbourne, C.D. (2007). The importance of social context: Neighbourhood stressors, stress buffering mechanisms and alcohol, drug and mental disorders. *Social Science & Medicine, 65*, 1867–1881.

9. Kalathil, J, Collier, B. Bhakta, R., Daniel, O. Joseph, D. & Trivedi, P. (2011). *Recovery and Resilience: African, African Caribbean and South Asian Women's Narratives of Recovering from Mental Distress.* London: Mental Health Foundation and Survivor Research. www.mentalhealth.org.uk/publications/recovery-and-resilience

10. Meddings, S. & Perkins, R. (2002). What 'getting better' means to staff and users of a rehabilitation service. *Journal of Mental Health, 11*, 319–325. http://informahealthcare.com/doi/pdf/10.1080/09638230020023697

11. Pitt, E., Kilbride, M., Nothard, S., Welford, M. & Morrison, A.P. (2007). Researching recovery from psychosis: a user-led project. *The Psychiatrist, 31*, 55–60. http://pb.rcpsych.org/content/31/2/55.full.pdf+html

12. Slade, M. (2010). Measuring recovery in mental health services. *Israel Journal of Psychiatry, 47*, 206–212. http://europepmc.org/abstract/MED/21149985

13. Greenwood, K., Sweeney, A., Williams, S., Garety, P., Kuipers, E., Scott, J. et al. (2010). CHoice of outcome in Cbt for psychosEs (CHOICE): The development of a new service user–led outcome measure of CBT for psychosis. *Schizophrenia Bulletin, 36*(1), 126-135. http://tinyurl.com/k6o4m68

14. Neil, S., Kilbride, M., Pitt, E., Nothard, S., Welford, M., Sellwood, W. et al. (2009). The questionnaire about the process of recovery (QPR): A measurement tool developed in collaboration with service users. *Psychosis: Psychological, Social and Integrative Approaches, 1*(2), 145–155. www.tandfonline.com/doi/pdf/10.1080/17522430902913450

15. Leamy, M., Bird, V., Le Boutillier, C., Williams, J. & Slade, M. (2011). Conceptual framework for personal recovery in mental health: systematic review and narrative synthesis. *British Journal of Psychiatry, 199*(6), 445–452. http://bjp.rcpsych.org/content/199/6/445.full.pdf+html

16. Lilly, R. (2005). About a psychiatrist. In A. Clare & S. Cuthbert (Eds.), *Developing practice in community mental health care. Trainers manual.* Brighton: Pavilion/Mental Health Foundation/City & Guilds Affinity.

17. Schrank, B., Bird, V., Rudnick, A. & Slade, M. (2012). Determinants, self-management strategies and interventions for hope in people with mental disorders: systematic search and narrative review. *Social Science and Medicine, 74*, 554–564. http://www.sciencedirect.com/science/article/pii/S0277953611007209

18. Warner, R. (1985). *Recovery from schizophrenia: Psychiatry and political economy.* London: Routledge, Kegan Paul.

19. Boydell, J., Bebbington, P., Bhavsar, V., Kravariti, E., van Os, J., Murray, R. M. et al. (2013). Unemployment, ethnicity and psychosis. *Acta Psychiatrica Scandinavica, 127*, 202–209. http://onlinelibrary.wiley.com/doi/10.1111/j.1600-0447.2012.01921.x/pdf

20. Rinaldi, M., Mcneil, K., Firn, M., Koletsi, M., Perkins, R. & Singh, S.P. (2004). What are the benefits of evidence-based supported employment for patients with first-episode psychosis. *The Psychiatrist, 28*, 281–284. http://pb.rcpsych.org/content/28/8/281.full.pdf+html

21. Prudo, R. & Blum, H.M. (1987). Five-year outcome and prognosis in schizophrenia: A report from the London Field Research Centre of the International Pilot Study of Schizophrenia. *The British Journal of Psychiatry, 150*(3), 345–354.

22. Angermeyer, M. & Schomerus, G. (2012). A stigma perspective on recovery. *World Psychiatry, 11*(3), 163–164. www.ncbi.nlm.nih.gov/pmc/articles/PMC3449353

23. Social Exclusion Unit (2004). *Mental health and social exclusion.* London: Office of The Deputy Prime Minister. www.nfao.org/Useful_Websites/MH_Social_Exclusion_report_summary.pdf

24. Wilkinson, R. & Pickett, K. (2010). *The spirit level: Why equality is better for everyone.* London: Penguin Books.

25. Tew, J., Ramon, S., Slade, M., Bird, V., Melton, J. & Le Boutillier, C. (2012). Social factors and recovery from mental health difficulties: a review of the evidence. *British Journal of Social Work, 42*, 443–460. http://bjsw.oxfordjournals.org/content/early/2011/06/15/bjsw.bcr076.full.pdf+html

26. Evert, H., Harvey, C., Trauer, T. & Herrman, H. (2003). The relationship between social networks and occupational and self-care functioning in people with psychosis. *Social Psychiatry and Psychiatric Epidemiology, 38*(4), 180–188. http://link.springer.com/article/10.1007/s00127-003-0617-4#

27. Topor, A., Borg, M., Mezzina, R., Sells, D., Marin, I. & Davidson, L. (2006). The role of family, friends and professionals in the recovery process. *American Journal of Psychiatric Rehabilitation, 9*(1), 17–37. http://recoverydevon.co.uk/download/Toporetal2006.pdf

28. Large, M., Nielssen, O., Slade, T. & Harris, A. (2008). Measurement and reporting of the duration of untreated psychosis. *Early Intervention in Psychiatry, 2*(1), 201–211. www.ncbi.nlm.nih.gov/pubmed/21352155

29. Taylor, P.J. & Gunn, J. (1999). Homicides by people with mental illness: Myth and reality. *British Journal of Psychiatry, 174*, 9–14. http://bjp.rcpsych.org/content/174/1/9.full.pdf+html

30. Large, M., Nielssen, O., Slade, T. & Harris, A. (2008). Measurement and reporting of the duration of untreated psychosis. *Early Intervention in Psychiatry, 2*(1), 201–211. http://onlinelibrary.wiley.com/doi/10.1111/j.1751-7893.2008.00080.x/pdf

31. Elbogen, E. & Johnson, S. (2009). The intricate link between violence and mental disorder. *Archives of General Psychiatry, 66*, 152–161. http://archpsyc.jamanetwork.com/article.aspx?articleid=210191

32. Tartakovsky, M. (2009). Media's damaging depictions of mental illness. Retrieved 30 January 2014 from http://psychcentral.com/lib/medias-damaging-depictions-of-mental-illness/0002220

33. CSIP/Shift (2006). *Mind over matter: Improving media reporting of mental health.* London: Sainsbury Centre for Mental Health, Mental Health Media, Rethink. www.centreformentalhealth.org.uk/pdfs/mindovermatter_summary.pdf

34. Time to Change (2013). *Soaps and dramas: Research.* Retrieved 30 January 2014 from www.time-to-change.org.uk/media-centre/media-advisory-service/soaps-dramas#research

35. Time to Change (2009). Screening madness: A century of negative movie stereotypes of mental illness. Retrieved 30 January 2014 from www.time-to-change.org.uk/sites/default/files/film-report-screening-madness-time-to-change.pdf

36. Pettitt, B., Greenhead, S., Khalifeh, H., Drennan, V., Hart, T., Hogg, J. et al. (2013). *At risk, yet dismissed.* London: Victim Support. www.victimsupport.org.uk/sites/default/files/At%20risk%20full.pdf

37. Boast, N. & Chesterman, P. (1995). Black people and secure psychiatric facilities: patterns of processing and the role of stereotypes. *British Journal of Criminology, 35*(2), 218-235.

38. Welsh, K. (2007). Black Criminal Stereotypes and Racial Profiling. *Journal of Contemporary Criminal Justice, 23*(3), 276-288.

39. Metzl, J. (2009). *The Protest Psychosis: How Schizophrenia became a Black Disease.* Boston: Beacon Press.

40. Mills, C. (2013). *Decolonizing Global Mental Health: The Psychiatrization of the Majority World.* London & New York: Routledge.

41. Fitzgibbon, D. (2007). Institutional racism, Pre-emptive criminalisation and risk analysis. *The Howard Journal of Crime and Justice, 46*(2), 128-144.

42. Read, J., Johnstone, L. & Taitimu, M. (2013). Psychosis, poverty and ethnicity. In J. Read & J. Dillon (Eds.) *Models of Madness: Psychological, Social and Biological Approaches to Psychosis.* London: Routledge.

43. Bhui, H.S. (1999). Race, racism and risk assessment: Linking theory to practice with black mentally disordered offenders. *Probation Journal, 46*(3), 171-181.

44. Special Hospitals Service Authority (SHSA) (1993). *Report of the Committee of Inquiry into the Death in Broadmoor Hospital of Orville Blackwood and a Review of the Deaths of Two Other Afro-Caribbean Patients: 'Big, black and Dangerous?'* (Chairman: Professor H. Prins) London: SHSA.

45. Thomas, P. (2012). Black and mad. Inquiry into the 'Schizophrenia' Label. Retrieved 12 December 2016 from www.schizophreniainquiry.org/news/black-and-mad

46. Keating, F., Robertson, D., McCulloch, A. & Francis, E. (2003). *Breaking the circles of fear: A review of the relationship between mental health services and African and Caribbean communities.* London: The Sainsbury Centre for Mental Health. Retrieved 20 December 2016 from www.offtherecordcroydon.org/media/4901/breaking_the_circles_of_fear.pdf

47. Keating, F. & Robertson, D. (2004). Fear, black people and mental illness: A vicious circle?. *Health and Social Care in the Community, 12*(5), 439-447.

Part 2

Introduction

1. Geekie, J. & Read, J. (2009). *Making sense of madness: Contesting the meaning of schizophrenia.* London: Routledge.

2. Bentall, R. P. (2003). *Madness explained: psychosis and human nature.* London: Penguin Books.

Section 5

1. Lilly UK. (2012, April). *Schizophrenia.* Retrieved 7 November 2013 from https://lilly.co.uk/your-health/schizophrenia

2. Holttum, S. (2014, February 20). *Seduced by biology: The BBC, black dog and biological bias.* Retrieved 24 April 2014, from http://discursiveoftunbridgewells.blogspot.co.uk/2014/02/seduced-by-biology-bbc-black-dog-and.html

3. Van Os, J., Rutten, B.P. & Poulton, R. (2008). Gene environment interactions in schizophrenia: review of epidemiological findings and future directions. *Schizophrenia Bulletin, 34*, 1066–1082. http://schizophreniabulletin.oxfordjournals.org/content/34/6/1066.full.pdf

4. Bentall, R. (2010). *Doctoring the mind: Why psychiatric treatments fail.* London: Penguin Books.

5. Crow, T. (2008). The emperors of the schizophrenia polygene have no clothes. *Psychological Medicine, 38*, 1681–1685.

6. Joseph, J. (2006). *The missing gene: Psychiatry, heredity and the fruitless search for genes.* New York: Algora Publishing.

7. Joseph, J. (2013). *The crumbling pillars of behavioral genetics.* Retrieved 18 April 2013 from www.councilforresponsiblegenetics.org/GeneWatch/GeneWatchPage.aspx?pageId=384

8. National Human Genome Research Institute (2013, 7 November). *Genome-wide association studies.* Retrieved 13 December 2013 from www.genome.gov./20019523

9.   Smoller, J.W., Craddock, N. & Kendler, K. (2013, April 20). Identification of risk loci with shared effects on five major psychiatric disorders: a genome-wide analysis. *The Lancet, 381*(9875), 1371–1379. http://www.sciencedirect.com/science/article/pii/S0140673612621291

10. Gallagher, J. (2013, Feb 28). *Five psychiatric disorders linked.* Retrieved 18 December 2013 from www.bbc.co.uk/news/health-21613924

11. Feilden, T. (2013, May 17). *Building a biological model of mental illness.* Retrieved 18 December 2013 from http://bbc.co.uk/news/science-environment-22566508

12. Hamshere, M.L., Stergiakouli, E., Langley, K., Martin, J., Holmans, P., Kent, L. et al. (2013, 1 Aug). A shared polygenic contribution between childhood ADHD and adult schizophrenia. *British Journal of Psychiatry, 203*, 81–83. http://bjp.rcpsych.org/content/203/2/107.full.pdf+html

13. Aron, E.N. (1999). *The highly sensitive person: How to thrive when the world overwhelms you.* London: Thorsons.

14. Van Os, J., Rutten, B.P. & Poulton, R. (2008). Gene environment interactions in schizophrenia: review of epidemiological findings and future directions. *Schizophrenia Bulletin, 34*, 1066–1082. http://schizophreniabulletin.oxfordjournals.org/content/34/6/1066.full.pdf+html

15. Kuepper, R., Morrison, P.D., van Os, J., Murray, R.M., Kenis, G. & Henquet, C. (2010, August). Does dopamine mediate the psychosis-inducing effects of cannabis? A review and integration of findings across disciplines. *Schizophrenia Research, 121*(1), 107–117. http://www.schres-journal.com/article/S0920-9964(10)01352-6/abstract

16. Howes, O.D. & Kapur, S. (2009, March 26). The dopamine hypothesis of schizophrenia: Version III – The final common pathway. *Schizophrenia Bulletin, 35*(3), 549–562. http://schizophreniabulletin.oxfordjournals.org/content/35/3/549.full.pdf+html

17. Howes, O.D. & Kapur, S. (2009, Match 26). The dopamine hypothesis of schizophrenia: Version III – The final common pathway. *Schizophrenia Bulletin, 35*(3), 549–562. http://schizophreniabulletin.oxfordjournals.org/content/35/3/549.full.pdf+html

18. Kapur, S. & Mamo, D. (2003, October). Half a century of antipsychotics and still a central role for dopamine D2 receptors. *Progress in Neuro-Psychopharmacology and Biological Psychiatry, 27*(7), 1081–1090. www.sciencedirect.com/science/article/pii/S0278584603002173

19. Geyer, M.A. & Vollenweider, F.X. (2008, Sept). Serotonin research: contributions to understanding psychoses. *Trends in Pharmacological Sciences, 29*(9), 445–453. www.sciencedirect.com/science/article/pii/S0165614708001545

20. Javitt, D.C. (2010). Glutamatergic theories of schizophrenia. *Israel Journal of Psychiatry and Related Sciences, 47*(1), 4–16. http://doctorsonly.co.il/wp- content/uploads/2011/12/2010_1_2.pdf

21. Weinberger, D. (2013). *Glutamate and schizophrenia.* Retrieved 18 December 2013 from www.dnalc.org/view/1173-Glutamate-and-Schizophrenia.html

22. Shenton, M.E., Whitford, T.J. & Kubicki, M. (2010, September). Structural neuroimaging in schizophrenia from methods to insights to treatments. *Dialogues in Clinical Neuroscience, 12*(3), 317–332. www.ncbi.nlm.nih.gov/pmc/articles/PMC3181976/pdf/DialoguesClinNeurosci-12-317.pdf

23. Kubicki, M., McCarley, R., Westin, C.F., Park, H.J., Maier, S., Kikinis, R. et al. (2007). A review of diffusion tensor imaging studies in schizophrenia. *Journal of Psychiatric Research, 41*(1), 15-30. www.sciencedirect.com/science/article/pii/S0022395605000671

24. Keshavan, M.S., Dick, E., Mankowski, I., Harenski, K., Montrose, D.M., Diwadkar, V. et al. (2002, December 1). Decreased left amygdala and hippocampal volumes in young offspring at risk for schizophrenia. *Schizophrenia Research, 58*(2-3), 173-183. http://www.sciencedirect.com/science/article/pii/S0920996401004042

25. Moncrieff, J. & Leo, J. (2010). A systematic review of the effects of antipsychotic drugs on brain volume. *Psychological Medicine, 40*, 1409-1422. http://journals.cambridge.org/action/displayAbstract?fromPage=online&aid=7863198

26. Maguire, E.A., Gadian, D.G., Johnsrude, I.S., Good, C.D., Ashburner, J., Frackowiak, R.S. et al. (2000). Navigation-related structural change in the hippocampi of taxi drivers. *Proceedings of the National Academy of Sciences of the United States of America, 97*(8), 4398-4403. www.pnas.org/content/97/8/4398.full

27. Hoy, K., Barrett, S. & Shannon, C. (2012). Childhood trauma and hippocampal and amygdalar volumes in first-episode psychosis. *Schizophrenia Bulletin, 38*(6), 112-1169. http://schizophreniabulletin.oxfordjournals.org/content/early/2011/07/28/ schbul.sbr085.full.pdf+html

28. Read, J. & Bentall, R.P. (2012). Negative childhood experiences and mental health: theoretical, clinical and primary prevention implications. *British Journal of Psychiatry, 200*, 89-91. http://bjp.rcpsych.org/content/200/2/89.full.pdf+html

29. Selten, J.-P., van der Ven, E., Rutten, B.P.F. & Cantor-Graee, E. (2013). The social defeat hypothesis of schizophrenia: An update. *Schizophrenia Bulletin, 134.* Retrieved 23 September 2013 from http://schizophreniabulletin.oxfordjournals.org/ content/early/2013/09/21/schbul.sbt134.abstract

30. Kumari, V. (2011). Sex differences and hormonal influences in human sensorimotor gating: Implications for schizophrenia. *Biological Basis of Sex Differences in Psychopharmacology, 8,* 141-154. www.ncbi.nlm.nih.gov/pubmed/21374020

31. American Psychiatric Association (2013). *Diagnostic and statistical manual of mental disorders* (5th edn.). Arlington, VA: American Psychiatric Publishing.

32. Kupfer, D. (2013). *Chair of DSM-5 Task Force responds to NIMH.* Retrieved 13 December 2013 from www.madinamerica.com/2013/05/chair-of-dsm-5-task-force-admits-lack-of-validity/

33. Boyle, M. (2004). Preventing a non-existent illness?: Some issues in the prevention of 'schizophrenia'. *Journal of Primary Prevention, 24*(4), 445-469. http://link.springer.com/article/10.1023%2FB%3AJOPP.0000024801.34886.a7#

34. Bentall, R.P. & Varese, F. (2012) A level playing field?: Are bio-genetic and psychosocial studies evaluated by the same standards? *Psychosis, 4*(3), 183-190. www.tandfonline.com/doi/pdf/10.1080/17522439.2012.729856

Section 6

1. Read, J., Magliano, L. & Beavan, V. (2013). Public beliefs about the causes of 'schizophrenia': Bad things happen and can drive you crazy. In J. Read & J. Dillon (Eds.), *Models of madness: Psychological, social and biological approaches to psychosis.* (pp.143–156). London: Routledge.

2. Sue, D.W. (2010). *Microaggressions in everyday life: Race, gender, and sexual orientation.* Hoboken, NJ: John Wiley & Sons.

3. Rhodes, J., Parrett, N. & Mason, O. (2015). A qualitative study of refugees with psychotic symptoms. *Psychosis*, 1–11. doi: 10.1080/17522439.2015.1045547

4. Jarrett, C. (2015, 10 August). What is it like to be a refugee with psychosis? [Blog post]. Research Digest. Retreived 14 December 2016 from http://digest.bps.org.uk/2015/08/what-is-it-like-to-be-refugee-with.html

5. Varese, F., Smeets, F. & Drukker, M. (2012). Childhood trauma increases the risk of psychosis: A meta analysis of patient-control, prospective and cross sectional cohort studies. *Schizophrenia Bulletin, 38*(4), 661–671. http://schizophreniabulletin.oxfordjournals.org/content/early/2012/03/28/ schbul.sbs050.full.pdf+html

6. Read, J. & Bentall, R.P. (2012). Negative childhood experiences and mental health: theoretical, clinical and primary prevention implications. *British Journal of Psychiatry, 200*, 89-91. http://bjp.rcpsych.org/content/200/2/89.full.pdf+html

7. Read, J., Fink, P.J., Rudegeair, T., Felitti V. & Whitfield, C.L. (2008, October). Child maltreatment and psychosis: A return to a genuinely integrated bio-psycho-social model. *Clinical Schizophrenia & Related Psychoses, 2*(3), 235–254: www.integration.samhsa.gov/pbhci-learning-community/child_maltreatment_and_psychosis.pdf

8. Bentall, R.P., Wickham, S., Shevlin, M. & Varese, F. (2012, April). Do specific early-life adversities lead to specific symptoms of psychosis? A study. *Schizophrenia Bulletin, 38*(4), 734-740. http://schizophreniabulletin.oxfordjournals.org/content/early/ 2012/04/09/schbul. sbs049.full.pdf+html

9. Kroll, J., Yusuf, A.I. & Fujiwara, K. (2011). Psychoses, PTSD, and depression in Somali refugees in Minnesota. *Social Psychiatry and Psychiatric Epidemiology, 46*, 481–493. http://schizophreniabulletin.oxfordjournals.org/content/early/ 2012/04/09/schbul.sbs049.full.pdf+html

10. Rudgeair, T. & Farrelly, S. (2008). Pharmocotherapy in the collaborative treatment of trauma-induced dissociation and psychosis. In I. Moskowitz, I. Schafer & M. J. Dorahy, *Psychosis, trauma and dissociation: Emerging perspectives on severe psychopathology* (pp.307–318). Oxford: Wiley-Blackwell.

11. Moskowitz, A., Read, J., Farrelly, S., Rudgeair, T. & Williams, O. (2009). Are psychotic symptoms traumatic in origin and dissociative in kind? In P.F. Dell & J.A. O'Neill, *Dissociation and the dissociative disorders: DSM-V and beyond.* (pp.521–534). New York: Routledge.

12. Longden, E., Madill, A. & Waterman, M.G. (2012). Dissociation, trauma and the role of the lived experience: Toward a new conceptulization of voice hearing. *Psychological Bulletin, 138*(1), 28–76. http://content.apa.org/journals/bul/138/1/28

13. Ross, C.A. (2012). Dissociative schizophrenia. In A. Moskowitz, I. Schafer, & M.J. Dorahy, *Psychosis, trauma and dissociation: Emerging perspectives on severe psychopathology* (pp.281–293). Oxford: Wiley-Blackwell.

14. Read, J. & Bentall, R.P. (2012). Negative childhood experiences and mental health: theoretical, clinical and primary prevention implications. *British Journal of Psychiatry, 200*, 89–91. http://bjp.rcpsych.org/content/200/2/89.full.pdf+html

15. Johnstone, L. (2011). Can traumatic events traumatize people? Trauma, madness and 'psychosis'. In M. Rapley, J. Moncrieff & J. Dillon, *De-medicalizing mental illness. psychology, psychiatry and the human condition.* (pp.99-109). Basingstoke: Palgrave Macmillan.

16. Josephine. (2012). *Personal accounts of paranoia.* (D. Freeman, Producer, & South London and Maudsley NHS Foundation Trust and Wellcome Trust) Retrieved 20 December 2013 from www.paranoidthoughts.com/accounts.php

17. Kalathil, J, Collier, B. Bhakta, R., Daniel, O. Joseph, D. & Trivedi, P. (2011). *Recovery and Resilience: African, African Caribbean and South Asian Women's Narratives of Recovering from Mental Distress.* London: Mental Health Foundation and Survivor Research. www. mentalhealth.org.uk/publications/recovery-and-resilience

18. Daan Marsman (2009) In M. Romme, S. Escher, J. Dillon, D. Corstens & M. Morris (2009). *Living with voices: 50 stories of recovery.* Ross-on-Wye: PCCS, p.15.

19. Janice. (2012). *Personal accounts of paranoia.* (D. Freeman, Producer, & South london and Maudsley NHS Foundation Trust and Wellcome Trust) Retrieved 20 December 2013 from www.paranoidthoughts.com/accounts.php

20. Read, J. & Sanders, P. (2010). *A straight talking introduction to the causes of mental health problems.* Ross-on-Wye: PCCS Books.

21. Kuipers, E., Onwumere, J. & Bebbington, P. (2010). Cognitive model of caregiving in psychosis. *British Journal of Psychiatry, 196*, 259–265. http://bjp.rcpsych.org/content/196/4/259.full.pdf+html

22. Sen, D. (2002). *The world is full of laughter.* Brentwood: Chipmunka Publishing.

23. Midlands Psychology Group (2012). Draft manifesto for a social materialist psychology of distress. *Journal of Critical Psychology, Counselling and Psychotherapy, 12*(2), 93–107. www.midpsy.org/draft_manifesto.htm

24. Rosenfield, S. (2012). Triple jeopardy? Mental health at the intersection of gender, race, and class. *Social Science & Medicine, 74*(1), 1791–1796.

25. Walby, S. (2007). Complexity theory, systems theory and multiple intersecting social inequalities. *Philosophy of the Social Sciences, 37*(4), 449–470.

26. Janssen, I., Hanssen, M., Bak, M., Bijl, R.V. et al. (2003). Discrimination and delusional ideation. *The British Journal of Psychiatry, 182*(1), 71–76.

27. Kirkbride, J.B., Jones, P.B., Ullrich, S. & Coid, J.W. (2012). Social deprivation, inequality, and the neighborhood-level incidence of psychotic syndromes in East London. *Schizophrenia Bulletin, 151.* http://schizophreniabulletin.oxfordjournals.org/content/40/1/169.full.pdf+html

28. Wilkinson, R. & Pickett, K. (2010). *The spirit level: Why equality is better for everyone.* London: Penguin Books.

29. Karlson, S., Nazroo, J.Y., McKenzie, K., Bhui, K. & Weich, S. (2005, December). Incidence of schizophrenia in ethnic minorities in London: Ecological study into interactions with environment. *Psychological Medicine, 35*(12), 1795–1803. http://journals.cambridge.org/action/displayAbstract?fromPage=online&aid=522892

30. Boydell, J., van Os, J., McKenzie, K., Allardyce, et al. (2001). Racism, psychosis and common mental disorder among ethnic minority groups in England. *British Medical Journal, 323,* 1336–1338.

31. Das-Munshi, J., Bécares, L., Boydell, J.E., Dewey, M.E., et al. (2012). Ethnic density as a buffer for psychotic experiences: Findings from a national survey (EMPIRIC). *The British Journal of Psychiatry, 201,* 282–290.

32. Shaw, R.J., Atkin, K., Bécares, L., Albor, C.B., et al. (2012). Impact of ethnic density on adult mental disorders: Narrative review. *The British Journal of Psychiatry, 201*(1), 11–19.

33. Heinz, A., Deserno, L & Reininghaus, U. (2013). Urbanicity, social adversity and psychosis. *World Psychiatry, 12*(3), 187–197.

34. Schwartz, R.C. & Blankenship, D.M. (2014). Racial disparities in psychotic disorder diagnosis: A review of empirical literature. *World Journal of Psychiatry, 4*(4), 133–140.

35. Neighbors, H.W., Trierweiler, S.J., Ford, B.C. & Muroff, J.R. (2003). Racial differences in DSM diagnosis using a semi-structured instrument: The importance of clinical judgment in the diagnosis of African Americans. *Journal of Health and Social Behavior, 44*(3), 237–256.

36. Care Quality Commission. (2010). *Count me in 2010. Results of the 2010 national census of inpatients and patients on supervised community treatment in mental health and learning disability services in England and Wales.* London: Care Quality Commission.

37. Commission for Healthcare Audit and Inspection. (2007). *Count me in. Results of the 2006 national census of inpatients in mental health and learning disability services in England and Wales.* London: Commission for Healthcare Audit and Inspection.

38. Special Hospitals Service Authority (SHSA) (1993). *Report of the Committee of Inquiry into the Death in Broadmoor Hospital of Orville Blackwood and a Review of the Deaths of Two Other Afro-Caribbean Patients: 'Big, black and Dangerous?'* (Chairman: Professor H. Prins) London: SHSA.

39. Davies, S.C. (2014). *Annual report of the Chief Medical Officer 2013, public mental health priorities: Investing in the evidence.* London: Department of Health.

40. Fernando, S. (2003). *Cultural diversity, mental health and psychiatry: The struggle against racism.* Hove: Brunner-Routledge.

41. Boast, N. & Chesterman, P. (1995). Black people and secure psychiatric facilities. *British Journal of Criminology, 35,* 218–235.

42. Lipsedge, M. & Littlewood, R. (1997). *Aliens and alienists: Ethnic minorities and psychiatry.* London: Routledge.

43. Dein, K., Williams, P.S. & Dein, S. (2007). Ethnic bias in the application of the Mental Health Act 1983. *Advances in Psychiatric Treatment, 13,* 350-357.

44. Keating, F. & Robertson, D. (2004). Fear, black people and mental illness: A vicious circle? *Health Soc Care Community, 12*(5), 439–447.

Section 7

1.   Pitt, E., Kilbride, M., Nothard, S., Welford, M. & Morrison, A.P. (2007). Researching recovery from psychosis: a user-led project. *The Psychiatrist, 31*, 55-60. http://pb.rcpsych.org/content/31/2/55.full.pdf+html

2.   Cromby, J. & Harper, D.J. (2009). Paranoia: a social account. *Theory and Psychology, 19*(3), 335-361. http://homepages.lboro.ac.uk/~hujc4/Paranoia%20a%20social%20account.pdf

3.   Bentall, R.P., Wickham, S., Shevlin, M. & Varese, F. (2012). Do specific early-life adversities lead to specific symptoms of psychosis? A study. *Schizophrenia Bulletin, 38*(4), 734-740. http://schizophreniabulletin.oxfordjournals.org/content/early/ 2012/04/09/schbul.sbs049.full. pdf+html

4.   McGuire, P.K., Murray, R.M. & Shah, G.M. (1993). Increased blood flow in Broca's area during auditory hallucinations. *Lancet, 342*, 703-706. www.sciencedirect.com/science/article/ pii/014067369391707S

5.   Waters, F., Allen, P., Aleman, A., Fernyhough, C., Woodward, T.S., Badcock, J.C. et al. (2012, June). Auditory hallucinations in schizophrenia and nonschizophrenia populations: a review and integrated model of cognitive mechanisms. *Schizophrenia Bulletin, 38*(4), 683-693. http://schizophreniabulletin.oxfordjournals.org/content/38/4/683.long

6.   Hayward, M. (2014). Interpersonal relating and voice hearing: To what extent does relating to the voice reflect social relating? *Psychology and Psychotherapy: Theory, Research and Practice, 76*(4), 369-383. www.ncbi.nlm.nih.gov/pubmed/14670187

7.   Longden, E. (2013, February 28). *Eleanor Longden: Learning from voices in my head.* Retrieved 11 July 2013 from www.ted.com/talks/eleanor_longden_the_voices_in_my_head

8.   Warman, D. & Martin, J.M. (2006). Cognitive insight and delusion proneness: an investigation using the Beck Cognitive Insight Scale. *Schizophrenia Research, 84*(2), 297-304. http://www.sciencedirect.com/science/article/pii/S0920996406000727

9.   Freeman, D., Garety, P.A., Kuipers, E., Fowler, D. & Bebbington, P.E. (2002). A cognitive model of persecutory delusions. *British Journal of Clinical Psychology, 41*, 331-347. http://onlinelibrary.wiley.com/doi/10.1348/014466502760387461/pdf

10.   Bentall, R.P., Corcoran, R., Howard, R., Blackwood, N. & Kinderman, P. (2001). Persecutory delusions: A review and theoretical integration. *Clinical Psychology Review, 21*(8), 1143-1192. http://www.sciencedirect.com/science/article/pii/S0272735801001064

11.   Garety P.A., Freeman, D., Jolley, S., Dunn, G., Bebbington, P., Fowler, D., Kuipers, E. & Dudley, R. (2005). Reasoning, emotions and delusional conviction in psychosis. *Journal of Abnormal Psychology 114*, 373-384. http://psycnet.apa.org/journals/abn/114/3/373/

12.   Dudley, R.E., John, C.H., Young, A.W. & Over, D.E. (1997). The effect of self referent-material on the reasoning of people with delusions. *British Journal of Clinical Psychology, 36*(4), 574-584. http://onlinelibrary.wiley.com/doi/10.1111/j.2044-8260.1997.tb01262.x/pdf

13.   Freeman, D. (2007, May). Suspicious minds: the psychology of persecutory delusions. *Clinical Psychology Review, 27*(4), 425-457. http://www.sciencedirect.com/science/article/pii/ S0272735806001553

14. Frith, C.D. & Corcoran, R. (1996, May). Exploring 'theory of mind' in people with schizophrenia. *Psychological Medicine, 26*(3), 521–530. http://journals.cambridge. org/download.php?file=%2FPSM%2FPSM26_03%2FS00332917000 35601a. pdf&code=020cabbb51bafa14e5fb4dfe7e2a40f0

15. Addington, J., Penn, D., Woods, S.W., Addington, D. & Perkins, D.O. (2008). Social functioning in individuals at clinical high risk for psychosis. *Schizophrenia Research, 99*(1–3), 119–124. http://tinyurl.com/lrj77va

16. Hemsley, D.R. (2005). The development of a cognitive model of schizophrenia: Placing it in context. *Neuroscience & Behavioral Reviews, 29*(6), 977–988. www.sciencedirect.com/science/ article/pii/S0149763405000849

17. Hepworth, C., Startup, H. & Freeman, D. (2011, September). Developing treatments of persistent persecutory delusions: the impact of an emotional processing and metacognitive awareness intervention. *Journal of Nervous & Mental Disease, 199*(9), 653–658. www.ncbi.nlm.nih.gov/pubmed/21878778

18. Adam. (2010, October 24). Experiencing suspicious thoughts and paranoia: An account. *Schizophrenia Bulletin, 37*(4), 656–658: http://schizophreniabulletin.oxfordjournals.org/ content/37/4/656.full?sid=0a3fbf23-648f- 4533-934f-7aa6abbd498c

19. May, R. (2001, February 6). *Taking a stand.* (F. Keane, interviewer) http://rufusmay.com/index. php?option=com_content&task=view&id=34&Itemid=29

20. Garety, P.A., Kuipers, E., Fowler, D., Freeman, D. & Bebbington, P.E. (2001). A cognitive model of the positive symptoms of psychosis. *Psychological Medicine, 31*, 189–195. http://eprints.ucl.ac.uk/7199/1/7199.pdf

21. Morrison, A.P. (2001, July). The interpretation of intrusions in psychosis: An integrative cognitive approach to hallucinations and delusions. *Behavioural and Cognitive Psychotherapy, 39*(3), 257–276. http://feltoninstitute.org/approach/ morrisonsinterpretationofintrusions.pdf

22. Peters, E., Lataster, T., Greenwood, K., Kuipers, E., Scott, J., Williams, S. et al. (2012). Appraisals, psychotic symptoms and affect in daily life. *Psychological Medicine, 42*, 1013–1023. http://journals.cambridge.org/download.php?file=%2FPSM%2FPSM42_05%2FS00332917110 01802a.pdf&code=a85f88eca646c3b1a69d566e33aeaf5e

23. Morrison, A.P. (2001, July). The interpretation of intrusions in psychosis: An integrative cognitive approach to hallucinations and delusions. *Behavioural and Cognitive Psychotherapy, 39*(3), 257–276. http://journals.cambridge.org/ action/displayAbstract;jsessionid=FE8DAA20534970E02306D6D A404E5A37. journals?fromPage=online&aid=80756

24. Morrison, A.P., Haddock, G. & Tarrier, N. (1995). Intrusive thoughts and auditory hallucinations: A cognitive approach. *Behavioural and Cognitive Psychotherapy, 23*, 265–280. http://journals.cambridge.org/action/displayAbstract?fromPage=online&aid=5091208

25. Poe, E.A. (1850). *Eleonora.* Retrieved 20 December 2013 from http://poestories.com/read/ eleonora

26. Slade, M. (2009). *Personal recovery and mental illness.* Cambridge: Cambridge University Press.

27. Kiser, S. (2004). An existential case study of madness: encounters with divine affliction. *Journal of Humanistic Psychology, 44*(4), 431–454. http://jhp.sagepub.com/content/44/4/431. full.pdf+html

28. Jackson, M. & Fulford, K.W. (2002). Psychosis good and bad: Values-based practice and the distinction between pathological and non-pathological forms of psychotic experience. *Philosophy, Psychiatry & Psychology, 9*(4), 387–394. http://muse.jhu.edu/ journals/ philosophy_psychiatry_and_psychology/v009/9.4jackson.pdf

29. Elam, J. (1999). *Dancing with God through the storm: Mysticism and mental illness.* Pendle Hill Publications.

30. Nelson, B. & Rawlings, D. (2010). Relating schizotypy and personality to the phenomonology of creativity. *Schizophrenia Bulletin, 36*(2), 388–399. www.ncbi.nlm.nih.gov/pmc/articles/ PMC2833116/pdf/sbn098.pdf

31. Fink, A., Weber, B., Koschutnig, K., Benedek, M., Reishofer, G., Ebner, F. et al. (2013). Creativity and schizotypy from the neuroscience perspective. *Cognitive, Affective & Behavioral Neuroscience.* Springer US: http://link.springer.com/article/10.3758/s13415-013-0210-6

32. Schuldberg, D., French, C., Stone, B.L. & Heberle, J. (1988). Creativity and schizotypal traits. Creativity test scores and perceptual aberration, magical ideation, and impulsive nonconformity. *Journal of Nervous and Mental Diseases, 176*(11), 648–657. http://journals.lww.com/jonmd/Abstract/1988/11000/Creativity_and_Schizotypal_Traits_Creat ivity_Test.2.aspx

33. The Icarus Project (2013). *The Icarus Project: Navigating the space between brilliance and madness.* Retrieved 11 November 2013 from the Icarus Project: www.theicarusproject.net

34. Clarke, I. (2001). *Psychosis and spirituality: Exploring the new frontier.* London: Whurr.

35. Cooke, A. & Brett, C. (submitted). Clinical psychologists' use of transformative models of psychosis – a grounded theory study. *Clinical Psychology and Psychotherapy.*

36. Nixon, G., Hagan, B. & Peters, T. (2010, October). Psychosis and transformation: A phenomenological inquiry. *International Journal of Mental Health and Addiction, 8*(4), 527–544. http://link.springer.com/article/10.1007%2Fs11469-009-9231-3#page-1

37. Cooke, A. & Brett, C. (submitted). Clinical psychologists' use of transformative models of psychosis – a grounded theory study. *Clinical Psychology and Psychotherapy.*

38. Romme, M. & Escher, S. (2012). *Psychosis as a personal crisis: an experience-based approach the international society for the psychological treatments of the schizophrenias and other psychoses.* Hove: Routledge.

39. Peters, E. (2001) Are delusions on a continuum? The case of religious and delusional beliefs. In I. Clarke (Ed.), *Psychosis and spirituality: Exploring the new frontier,* (pp.191–207). London and Philadelphia: Whurr.

40. Perkins, R. (2006). First person: 'You need hope to cope'. In G. Roberts, S. Davenport, F. Holloway & T. Tattan, *Enabling recovery: the principles and practice of rehabilitation psychiatry* (pp.112–126). London: Royal College of Psychiatrists.

41. Holly. In C. Heriot-Maitland, M. Knight & E. Peters (2012). A qualitative comparison of psychotic-like phenomena in clinical and non-clinical populations. *British Journal of Clinical Psychology, 51*(1), 37–53, p.46. http://onlinelibrary.wiley.com/doi/10.1111/j.2044-8260.2011.02011.x/pdf

42. Parker, U. (1999). *The courage to bare our souls: a collection of pieces written out of mental distress.* London: Mental Health Foundation.

43. Nicholls, V. (2007). Connecting past and present: a survivor reflects on spirituality and mental health. In M.E. Coyte, P. Gilbert & V. Nicholls (Eds.), *Spirituality, values and mental health: Jewels for the journey* (p.102). London: Jessica Kingsley.

44. Spiritual Crisis Network (2014). *From breakdown to breakthrough: Promoting understanding and support.* Retrieved 11 November 2013 from www.spiritualcrisisnetwork.org.uk/

45. Clarke, I. (2010). *Psychosis and spirituality: Consolidating the new paradigm* (2nd edn.). London: Wiley Blackwell.

46. Clarke, I. (2008). *Madness, mystery and the survival of God.* Ropely: O Books.

47. Clarke, I. (2010). *Psychosis and spirituality: Consolidating the new paradigm* (2nd edn.). London: Wiley Blackwell.

48. Cooke, A. & Brett, C. (submitted). Clinical psychologists' use of transformative models of psychosis – a grounded theory study. *Clinical Psychology and Psychotherapy.*

49. Clarke, I. (2010). *Psychosis and spirituality: Consolidating the new paradigm* (2nd edn.). London: Wiley Blackwell.

50. Clay, S. (1999). Madness and reality. In P. Barker, P. Campbell & B. Davidson (Eds.), F*rom the ashes of experience – reflections of madness, survival and growth.* (pp.16–36). London: Whurr.

51. Kalathil, J. (2011). *Recovery and Resilience: African, African-Caribbean and South Asian women's narratives of recovering from mental distress.* Retrieved 1 December 2016 from www.mentalhealth.org.uk/publications/recovery-and-resilience/

52. Campbell, P. (2010). Surviving the system. In T. Basset & T. Stickley (Eds.), *Voices of experience: Narratives of mental health survivors* (p.22). Chichester: Wiley-Blackwell.

Part 3

Section 8

1. Johnstone, L. & Dallos, R. (2013). *Formulation in psychology and psychotherapy.* Hove: Routledge.

2. Butler, G. (1998). Clinical formulation. In A.S. Bellack & M. Hersen (Eds.), *Comprehensive clinical psychology.* Oxford: Pergamon.

3. Division of Clinical Psychology (2011). *Good practice guidelines on the use of psychological formulation.* Leicester: British Psychological Society. Available from http://shop.bps.org.uk/ good-practice-guidelines-on-the-use-of-psychological- formulation.html

4. Division of Clinical Psychology (2011). *Good practice guidelines on the use of psychological formulation.* Leicester: British Psychological Society. Available from http://shop.bps.org.uk/ good-practice-guidelines-on-the-use-of-psychological- formulation.html

5. Division of Clinical Psychology (2011). *Good practice guidelines on the use of psychological formulation.* Leicester: British Psychological Society. Available from http://shop.bps.org.uk/ good-practice-guidelines-on-the-use-of-psychological- formulation.html

6. May, R. (nd). *Understanding psychotic experience and working towards recovery.* Retrieved 18 June 2014 from www.rufusmay.com/index.php?option=com_ content&task=view&id=30&Itemid=33

7. Bentall, R. (2003). *Madness explained: Psychosis and human nature,* p.141. London, New York: Penguin.

8. Longden, E. (2010). Making sense of voices: A personal story of recovery. *Psychosis: Psychological, Social and Integrative Approaches, 2*(3), 255–259. www.tandfonline.com/doi/pdf/10.1080/17522439.2010.512667

9. Napier, D., Ancarno, C., Butler, B. & Calabrese, J., et al. (2014). Culture and health. *The Lancet, 384*(9954), 1607–1639. www.thelancet.com/journals/lancet/article/PIIS0140-6736(14)61603-2/fulltext

10. Lewis-Fernández, R. & Aggarwal, N. (2014). Cultural Formulation Interview Project. Retrieved 15 December 2016 from www.criticalpsychiatry.net/wp-content/uploads/2010/01/Clinical-appeal-of-cultural-formulations-in-rural-mental-health-a-manual.pdf

Section 9

1. Faulkner, A. & Layzell, S. (2000). *Strategies for living.* London: Mental Health Foundation. www.mentalhealth.org.uk/content/assets/PDF/publications/ strategies_for_living_summary. pdf?view=Standard

2. Rethink Mental Illness (2013). *Rethink mental illness.* Retrieved 20 December 2013 from www.rethink.org/?gclid=CJevo5O1mbsCFW_MtAodCCwArQ

3. Sayce, E. (2000). F*rom psychiatric patient to citizen: Overcoming discrimination and social exclusion.* New York: St Martin's Press.

4. Kuipers, E., Onwumere, J. & Bebbington, P. (2010). Cognitive model of caregiving in psychosis. *British Journal of Psychiatry, 196,* 259–265. http://bjp.rcpsych.org/content/196/4/259.full. pdf+html

5. Jen. (2013, February 15). *My friends and family supported me after a psychotic episode.* Retrieved 11 July 2013 from www.time-to-change.org.uk/blog/psychotic-episode-friends-family-support

6. Kuipers, E., Onwumere, J. & Bebbington, P. (2010). Cognitive model of caregiving in psychosis. *British Journal of Psychiatry, 196,* 259–265. http://bjp.rcpsych.org/content/196/4/259.full.pdf+html

7. Slade, M., Pinfold, V., Rapaport, J., Bellringer, S., Banerjee, S., Kuipers, E. et al. (2007). Best practice when service users do not consent to sharing information with carers – National multimethod study. *British Journal of Psychiatry, 190,* 148–155. http://bjp.rcpsych.org/content/190/2/148.full.pdf+html

8. Meddings, S., Gordon, I. & Owen, D. (2010). Family and systemic work. In R*eaching out: The psychology of assertive outreach.* London: Routledge.

9. Seikkula, J. & Arnkil, T.E. (2006). *More about open dialogues: Dialogical meetings in social networks.* London: Karnac Books.

10. Fadden, G., James , C. & Pinfold, V. (2012). *Caring for yourself – self help for families and friends supporting people with mental health problems.* Birmingham: White Halo Design.

11. Meddings, S., Gordon, I. & Owen, D. (2010). Family and systemic work. In *Reaching out: The psychology of assertive outreach.* London: Routledge.

12. National Institute for Health and Care Excellence (2014). *Psychosis and schizophrenia in adults: treatment and management. NICE clinical guidelines.* London: National Institute for Health and Care Excellence. www.nice.org.uk/nicemedia/live/14382/66534/66534.pdf

13. Schizophrenia Commission (2012). *The abandoned illness: A report from the Schizophrenia Commission.* London: Rethink Mental Illness. www.rethink.org/media/514093/TSC_main_report_14_nov.pdf

14. Stanbridge, R.I., Burbach, F.R., Lucas, A.S. & Carter, K. (2003, May). A study of families' satisfaction with a family interventions in psychosis service in Somerset. *Journal of Family Therapy, 25*(2), 181–204. http://onlinelibrary.wiley.com/doi/10.1111/1467-6427.00243/pdf

15. Cromby, J. & Harper, D. (2013). Paranoia: Contested and contextualised. In S. Coles, S. Keenan & B. Diamond (Eds.), *Madness contested: Power and practice.* Ross-on-Wye: PCCS books.

16. Mackler, D. (2013). *Trailer for 'Open Dialogue', an alternative Finnish approach to healing psychosis.* YouTube clip. Finland: www.youtube.com/watch?v=aBjlvnRFja4

17. Seikkula, J. & Arnkil, T.E. (2006). *More about open dialogues: Dialogical meetings in social networks.* London: Karnac Books.

18. Seikkula, J., Aaltonnen, J., Alakare, B., Haarakangus, K., Keranen, J. & Lehtinen, K. (2006). Five year experience of first-episode non-affective psychosis in open-dialogue approach: Treatment principles, follow-up outcomes, and two case studies. *Psychotherapy Research, 16*(2), 214–228. http://psychrights.org/research/digest/effective/fiveyarocpsychotherapyresearch.pdf

19. Cave, J. (2010). Self-help. In T. Basset, & T. Stickley (Eds.), *Voices of experience: Narratives of mental health Survivors* (p.142). Chichester: Wiley-Blackwell.

20. Kalathil, J. (2011). *Recovery and Resilience: African, African-Caribbean and South Asian women's narratives of recovering from mental distress.* Retrieved 1 December 2016 from www.mentalhealth.org.uk/publications/recovery-and-resilience/

21. Seebohm, P., Henderson, P., Munn-Giddings, C., Thomas, P. & Yasmeen, S. (2005). T*ogether we will change: Community development, mental health and diversity – Learning from challenge and achievement at Sharing Voices* (Bradford). London: The Sainsbury Centre for Mental Health.

22. Campbell, P. (2010). Surviving the system. In T. Basset & T. Stickley (Eds.), *Voices of experience: Narratives of mental health survivors* (p.29). Chichester: Wiley-Blackwell.

23. Meddings, S., Stapley, J. & Tredgett, C. (2010). Working in partnership with service user colleagues to develop self-help hearing voices groups. *Clinical Psychology Forum, 209,* 28–31.

24. Sheffield Hearing Voices Network (2013). *Hearing Voices Network: for people who hear voices, see visions or have other unusual perceptions.* Retrieved 7 November 2013 from www.hearing-voices.org

25. Longden, E., Corstens, D. & Dillon, J. (2013). Recovery, discovery and revolution: The work of Intervoice and the Hearing Voices Movement. In S. Coles, S. Keenan & B. Diamond (Eds.). *Madness contested: Power and practice.* Ross-on-Wye: PCCS Books.

26. Sheffield Hearing Voices Network (2013). Hearing Voices Network. Retrieved 5 December 2013 from www.hearing-voices.org/

27. Sen, D. (2006). *The World is Full of Laughter (Memoir on Mental Distress).* London: Chipmunka Publishing.

28. Mead, S. (2012). *Peer support in mental health and learning disability.* Retrieved 7 November 2013 from www.mentalhealth.org.uk/content/assets/PDF/publications/ need_2_know_peer_support1.pdf

29. Bradstreet, S. (2006). Harnessing the 'lived experience'. Formalising peer support approaches to remote recovery. *Mental Health Review, 11*(2), 33–37. http://tinyurl.com/p2s6k9w

30. Basset, T., Faulkner, A., Repper, J. & Stamou, E. (2010). *Lived experience leading the way. Together for mental wellbeing.* Together/NSUN.University of Nottingham. www.together-uk.org/wp-content/uploads/downloads/2011/11/livedexperiencereport.pdf

31. Wallcraft, J., Read, J. & Sweeney, A. (2003). *On our own terms. Users and survivors of mental health services working together for support and change.* The Sainsbury Centre for Mental Health. www.centreformentalhealth.org.uk/pdfs/on_our_own_terms.pdf

32. National Institute for Health and Care Excellence (2014). *Psychosis and schizophrenia in adults: Treatment and management. NICE clinical guidelines.* London: National Institute for Health and Care Excellence. www.nice.org.uk/nicemedia/live/14382/66534/66534.pdf

33. Mental Health Foundation. (2012, August). *Peer support in mental health and learning disability.* London: Mental Health Foundation. www.mentalhealth.org.uk/content/ assets/PDF/ publications/need_2_know_peer_support1.pdf?view=Standard

34. Repper, J. & Carter, T. (2010). Using personal experience to support others with similar difficulties. Together/University of Nottingham/NSUN. www.together-uk.org/wp-content/ uploads/downloads/2011/11/usingpersexperience.pdf

35. Faulkner, A. & Kalathil, J. (2012). *The freedom to be, the chance to dream: Preserving user-led peer support in mental health.* Together for mental wellbeing. www.together-uk.org/wp-content/uploads/2012/09/The-Freedom-to-be-The-Chance-to-dream-Full-Report1.pdf

36. Davidson, L., Bellamy, C., Guy, K. & Miller, R. (2012, June). Peer support among persons with severe mental illnesses: a review of evidence and experience. *World Psychiatry, 11*(2), 123–128. www.ncbi.nlm.nih.gov/pmc/articles/PMC3363389/pdf/wpa020123.pdf

37. Sainsburys Centre for Mental Health (2009, September). *Implementing recovery: a new framework for organisational change.* Retrieved 11 November 2013 from www.centreformentalhealth.org.uk/pdfs/implementing_recovery_paper.pdf

38. Watson, E. (2012). One year in peer support – personal reflections. *Journal of Mental Health Training Education and Practice, 7*(2), 85–88. www.emeraldinsight.com/journals.htm?articleid=17037226&show=abstract

39. Ledwith, M. (2011). *Community Development: A critical approach.* Bristol: Policy Press.

40. Seebohm, P., Henderson, P. & Munn-Giddings C. (2005). *Together We Will Change: Community Development, Mental Health and Diversity.* London: Sainsbury Centre for Mental Health.

41. Kalathil, J. (2011). *Recovery and Resilience: African, African-Caribbean and South Asian women's narratives of recovering from mental distress.* Retrieved 1 December 2016 from www.mentalhealth.org.uk/publications/recovery-and-resilience/

42. Seebohm, P. & Gilchrist, A. (2008). *Connect and Include: An exploratory study of community development and mental health.* London: National Social Inclusion Programme.

43. Seebohm, P. & Gilchrist, A. (2008). *Connect and Include: An exploratory study of community development and mental health.* London: National Social Inclusion Programme.

44. Penn, D.L., Uzenoff, S.R., Perkins, D., Mueser, K.T., Hamer, R., Waldheter, E. et al. (2012). A pilot investigation of the Graduated Recovery Intervention Programme (GRIP) for first episode psychosis. *Schizophrenia Research, 141*(1), 106–107. www.sciencedirect.com/science/article/pii/S0920996410014520

45. Perkins, R. & Slade, M. (2012). Recovery in England: Transforming statutory services? *International Review of Psychiatry, 24*(1), 29–39: http://informahealthcare.com/doi/pdf/10.3109/09540261.2011.645025

46. Repper, J., Perkins, R., Shepherd, G. & Boardman, J. (2011). *A personal health and well-being plan for family, friends and carers. ImRoc Implementing Recovery – Organisational change.* NHS Confederation/National Mental Health Development Unit/Centre for Mental Health. www.recoverydevon.co.uk/download/ImROC_Family_health_and_well-being_plan_version_1_final.pdf

47. Perkins, R., Repper, J., Rinaldi, M. & Brown, H. (2012). *Recovery Colleges. Implementing Recovery through Organisational Change (ImROC) briefing paper.* London: Centre for Mental Health. www.centreformentalhealth.org.uk/pdfs/Recovery_Colleges.pdf

48. Wybourn, S. & Rinaldi, M. (2011). *The Recovery College Pilot in Merton and Sutton: Longer term individual and service level outcomes.* Wandsworth: Wandsworth Borough Council.

49.   Rinaldi, M. & Suleman, M. (2012). *Care co-ordinators attitudes to self-management and their experience of the use of the South West London Recovery College.* London: South West London and St George's Mental Health NHS Trust.

50.   Sussex Partnership NHS Foundation Trust (2013, May 30). *Hastings & Rother Recovery College Open Day 6 June 2013.* Retrieved 31 January 2014, from Sussex Partnership NHS Foundation Trust: www.sussexpartnership.nhs.uk/about/news/articles/610-college-open-day

51.   Beresford, P. (2013). Experiential Knowledge and the Reconception of Madness. In S. Coles, S. Keenan & R. Diamond, *Madness contested: power and practice.* Ross-on-Wye: PCCS Books.

52.   Network for Mental Health (2013). *Network of mental health.* Retrieved 7 November 2013 from www.nsun.org.uk

Section 10

1.   Slade, M. (2010). Mental illness and well-being: the central importance of positive psychology and recovery approaches. *BMC Health Services Research, 10*(26). www.biomedcentral.com/1472-6963/10/26

2.   Beresford, P. (2012). *Recovery 2012.* Retrieved 21 May 2014 from www.vimeo.com/41967871

3.   Harper, D. & Speed, E. (2012). *Uncovering recovery: The resistible rise of recovery and resilience.* Retrieved 21 May 2014 from www.ojs.uwindsor.ca/ojs/leddy/index.php/SSJ/article/view/3499

4.   Slade, M. (2009). *Personal recovery and mental illness.* Cambridge: Cambridge University Press.

5.   Slade, M., Amering, M., Farkas, M., Hamilton, B., O'Hagan, M., Panther, G. et al. (2014). Uses and abuses of recovery: implementing recovery-oriented practices in mental health systems. *World Psychiatry, 13*(1), 12–20. http://onlinelibrary.wiley.com/doi/10.1002/wps.20084/pdf

6.   Machin, K. & Repper, J. (2013, June 4). *Recovery: a carer's perspective.* Retrieved 21 May 2014 from www.nhsconfed.org/resources/2013/06/4-recovery-a-carers-perspective

7.   Harper, D. & Speed, E. (2012). *Uncovering recovery: The resistible rise of recovery and resilience.* Retrieved 21 May 2014 from www.ojs.uwindsor.ca/ojs/leddy/index.php/SSJ/article/view/3499

8.   Shepherd, G., Boardman, J. & Slade, M. (2008, March 17). *Making recovery a reality.* Retrieved 7 March 2014 from www.centreformentalhealth.org.uk/pdfs/Making_recovery_a_reality_policy_paper.pdf

9.   Shepherd, G., Boardman, J. & Slade, M. (2008, March 17). *Making recovery a reality.* Retrieved 7 March 2014 from www.centreformentalhealth.org.uk/pdfs/Making_recovery_a_reality_policy_paper.pdf

10.   Mental Health Network NHS Confederation (2012, June). *Supporting recovery in mental health – Briefing paper.* Retrieved 7 November 2013 from http://nhsconfed.org/ Publications/ Documents/Supporting_recovery_in_mental_health.pdf

11.   Shepherd, G., Boardman, J., & Burns, M. (2010). Implementing recovery: A methodology for organisational change. Sainsbury Centre for Mental Health. www.nhsconfed.org/NETWORKS/ MENTALHEALTH/PROJECTS-AND- RESOURCES/IMROC/Pages/Implementing-Recovery-Organisational-Change-Project.aspx

12. Copeland, M.E. (1995, 2014). *WRAP and recovery books.* Retrieved 31 January 2014 from www.mentalhealthrecovery.com/wrap/

13. Mental Health Foundation (2014). *Diet and mental health.* Retrieved 31 January 2014 from www.mentalhealth.org.uk/help-information/mental-health-a-z/D/diet/

14. Freeman, D., Stahl, D., McManus, S., Meltzer, H., Brugha, T., Wiles, N. et al. (2012). Insomnia, worry, anxiety and depression as predictors of the occurrence and persistence of paranoid thinking. *Social Psychiatry and Psychiatric Epidemiology, 47*(8), 1195–203. http://link.springer.com/article/10.1007%2Fs00127-011-0433-1

15. Myers, E., Startup, H. & Freeman, D. (2011). Cognitive behavioural treatment of insomnia in individuals with persistent persecutory delusions: A pilot trial. *Journal of Behaviour Therapy and Experimental Psychiatry, 42*(3), 330–336. http://www.sciencedirect.com/science/article/pii/S0005791611000279

16. Springham, N. & Woods, A. (2014, January 7). *Toolkit uses patient experiences to improve mental health services.* Retrieved 16 January 2014, from www.theguardian.com/healthcare-network/2014/jan/07/mental-health-toolkit-improves-services

17. Allan, C. (2009, January 14). *My brilliant survival guide.* Retrieved 31 January 2014 from www.theguardian.com/society/2009/jan/14/mental-health-clare-allan-social-worker

18. Sen, D. (2002). *The world is full of laughter.* Brentwood: Chipmunka Publishing.

19. Cobb, A. (1993). *Safe and effective? MIND's view on psychiatric drugs, ECT and psychosurgery,* p.26. London: MIND.

20. Chadwick, P.K. (1997). *Schizophrenia: The positive perspective.* London: Routledge.

21. Grove, B., Secker, J. & Seebohm, P. (Eds.). (2005). *New thinking about mental health and employment.* Oxford: Radcliffe Publishing Ltd.

22. Schizophrenia Commission. (2012). *The abandoned illness: A report from the Schizophrenia Commission.* London: Rethink Mental Illness. www.rethink.org/media/514093/TSC_main_report_14_nov.pdf

23. National Institute for Health and Care Excellence (2014). *Psychosis and schizophrenia in adults: treatment and management. NICE clinical guidelines.* London: National Institute for Health and Care Excellence. www.nice.org.uk/nicemedia/live/14382/66534/66534.pdf

24. Grove, B., Secker, J. & Seebohm, P. (Eds.). (2005). *New thinking about mental health and employment.* Oxford: Radcliffe Publishing Ltd.

25. Mental Health Europe (2013). *A chance to thrive.* YouTube. (S. Enculescu, & Y. Brand, Eds.) GB. Retrieved 20 March 2014 from www.youtube.com/watch?v=wTGDDGJT-M4

26. Sainsbury Centre for Mental Health (2009). *41: Commissioning what works, the economic and financial case for supported employment.* London: Sainsbury Centre for Mental Health. www.centreformentalhealth.org.uk/pdfs/briefing41_commissioning_what_works.pdf

27. Campbell, K., Bond, G.R. & Drake, R.E. (2011). Who benefits from supported employment: a meta-analyticstudy. *Schizophrenia Bulletin, 37*(2), 370–380. http://schizophreniabulletin.oxfordjournals.org/content/37/2/370.full.pdf+html

28. Crowther, R., Marshall, M., Bond, G.R., & Huxley, P. (2010). *Vocational rehabilitation for people with severe mental illness (Review)*. Cochrane Library, 2010(11). http://onlinelibrary. wiley.com/doi/10.1002/14651858.CD003080/pdf

29. Wooldridge, J. (2011, October 24). *My employment journey.* Retrieved 7 March 2014 from www.time-to-change.org.uk/blog/my-employment-journey

30. *Equality Act 2010.* www.legislation.gov.uk/ukpga/2010/15/pdfs/ukpga_20100015_en.pdf

31. Time to Change (2013). *Legal Decisions: mental health discrimination test cases.* Retrieved 11 November 2013 from www.time-to-change.org.uk/your-organisation/support- employers/ legal-decisions-important-case-reports

32. Henderson, C., Brohan, E., Clement, S., Williams, P., Lassman, F., Schauman, O. et al. (2012). A decision aid to assist decisions on disclosure of mental health status to an employer: protocol for the CORAL exploratory randomised controlled trial. *BMC Psychiatry, 12,* 133. www.biomedcentral.com/content/pdf/1471-244X-12-133.pdf

33. Whitaker, R. (2011, February 8). *Mad in America.* Retrieved 21 May 2014 from www. psychologytoday.com/blog/mad-in-america/201102/andreasen-drops-bombshell- antipsychotics-shrink-the-brain

34. Leff, J.P. & Warner, R. (2006). *Social inclusion of people with mental illness.* Cambridge: Cambridge University Press.

35. Rinaldi, M., Mcneil, K., Firn, M., Koletsi, M., Perkins, R. & Singh, S.P. (2004). What are the benefits of evidence-based supported employment for patients with first-episode psychosis? *The Psychiatrist, 28,* 281–284. http://pb.rcpsych.org/content/28/8/281.full.pdf+html

36. Wykes, T., Huddy, V., Cellard, C., McGurk, S.R. & Czobor, P. (2011). A meta-analysis for cognitive remediation for schizophrenia: methodology and effect sizes. *American Journal of Psychiatry, 168*(5), 472–485. http://ajp.psychiatryonline.org/data/Journals/AJP/3938/appi. ajp.2010.10060855.pdf

37. National Institute for Health and Care Excellence (2014). *Psychosis and schizophrenia in adults: treatment and management. NICE clinical guidelines.* London: National Institute for Health and Care Excellence. www.nice.org.uk/nicemedia/live/14382/66534/66534.pdf

38. Schizophrenia Commission (2012). *The abandoned illness: A report from the Schizophrenia Commission.* London: Rethink Mental Illness. www.rethink.org/media/514093/TSC_main_ report_14_nov.pdf

39. Morrison, A., French, P., Walford, L., Lewis, S., Kilcommons, A., Green, J. et al. (2004). Cognitive therapy for the prevention of psychosis in people at ultra-high risk: randomised controlled trial. *British Journal of Psychiatry, 185,* 291–297. http://bjp.rcpsych.org/content/185/4/291. full.pdf+html

40. Grey, S.J. (2007). A structured problem-solving group for psychiatric inpatients. *Groupwork, 17*(1), 20–33. http://essential.metapress.com/content/a155166l53n37852/

41. Sussex Partnership NHS Foundation Trust (2014). *Myth busting information about mental health, unusual distressing experiences and early intervention.* Retrieved 24 April 2014 from www.isanyoneelselikeme.org.uk/

42. Morrison, A., French, P., Walford, L., Lewis, S., Kilcommons, A., Green, J. et al. (2004). Cognitive therapy for the prevention of psychosis in people at ultra-high risk: randomised controlled trial. *British Journal of Psychiatry, 185,* 291–297. http://bjp.rcpsych.org/content/185/4/291. full.pdf+html

43. Greater Manchester West Mental Health NHS Foundation Trust & University of Manchester (2014). *Psychosis Research Unit.* Retrieved 24 April 2014 from www.psychosisresearch.com/

44. Schizophrenia Commission (2012). *The abandoned illness: A report from the Schizophrenia Commission.* London: Rethink Mental Illness. www.rethink.org/media/514093/TSC_main_ report_14_nov.pdf

45. Springham, N. & Woods, A. (2014, January 07). *Toolkit uses patient experiences to improve mental health services.* Retrieved 16 January 2014 from www.theguardian.com/healthcare- network/2014/jan/07/mental-health-toolkit-improves-services

46. Star Wards. (2014). *Star wards.* Retrieved 7 February 2014 from www.starwards.org.uk/

47. MIND (2011). *Listening to experience: An independent inquiry into acute and crisis mental healthcare.* London: MIND publications. www.mind.org.uk/media/211306/listening_to_ experience_web.pdf

48. Springham, N. & Woods, A. (2014, January 07). *Toolkit uses patient experiences to improve mental health services.* Retrieved 16 January 2014 from www.theguardian.com/healthcare- network/2014/jan/07/mental-health-toolkit-improves-services

49. Johnson, S., Gilburt, H., Lloyd-Evans, B., Osborn, D.P., Boardman, J., Leese, M. et al. (2009). In- patient and residential alternatives to standard acute psychiatric wards in England. British *Journal of Psychiatry, 194,* 456–463. http://bjp.rcpsych.org/content/194/5/456.full.pdf

50. Camden and Islington NHS Foundation Trust (2013). *Drayton Park Women's Crisis Service.* Retrieved 18 July 2013 from www.candi.nhs.uk/services/services/drayton-park-womens-crisis- service/

51. South London and Maudsley NHS Foundation Trust (2013). *Foxley Lane Women's Services (Croydon).* Retrieved 11 Nov ember 2013 from www.slam.nhs.uk/our-services/service-finder- details?CODE=SU0131

52. Rethink Mental Illness (2012, July). *Event marks official launch of new recovery houses for people with mental illness in north London.* Retrieved 18 June 2014 from www.rethink.org/ media-centre/2012/07/event-marks-official-launch-of-new-recovery- houses-for-people- with-mental-illness-in-north-london

53. Hertfordshire Partnership University NHS Foundation Trust (nd). *Host families scheme.* Retrieved 21 May 2014 from www.hpft.nhs.uk/our-services/acute-services/host-families- scheme/

54. Wokingham Mental Health Association (2013). *Wokingham Mental Health Association.* Retrieved 11 November 2013 from www.wokinghammentalhealth.org.uk/

55. Leeds Survivor Led Crisis Service (2013). *Leeds Survivor Led Crisis Service: Sanctuary and support in times of crisis.* Retrieved 12 December 2013 from www.lslcs.org.uk/

56. Johnson, S. (2014). *Alternatives to hospitals. Refocus on Recovery: International Conference.* London: www.researchintorecovery.com/files/RoR2014-Timetable%20online%20version_5.pdf

57.   Allan, C. (2006, October 4). *A rare place to face my seasonal demons.* Retrieved 18 July 2013 from www.guardian.co.uk/society/2006/oct/04/socialcare.comment1

58.   Kent and Medway NHS and Social Care Partnership Trust (2011). *Advanced directive.* www.kmpt.nhs.uk/Downloads/Understanding-Mental-Health/leaflets/Advanced-Directive-Easy-Read.pdf

59.   Evans, J.J., Chua, S.E., McKenna, P.J. & Wilson, B.A. (1997). Assessment of the dysexecutive syndrome in schizophrenia. *Psychological Medicine, 27*(3), 635–646. http://journals.cambridge.org/download.php?file=%2FPSM%2FPSM27_03%2FS00332917970 04790a.pdf&code=5a126e9e31b77b2d90aecae20ceafeb1

60.   Rethink Mental Illness Advice and Information Service (2014). *Advocacy.* Retrieved 7 February 2014 from www.rethink.org/living-with-mental-illness/rights-restrictions/advocacy

61.   Department of Health/National Statistics (2010). *In-patients formally detained in hospitals under the Mental Health Act 1983 and patients subject to supervised community treatment. Annual figures, England 2009/10.* London: Health and Social Care Information Centre, Community and Mental Health Team. www.hscic.gov.uk/catalogue/PUB12503/inp-det-m-h-a-1983-sup-com-eng-12-13-rep.pdf

62.   MIND (2015). *Restraint in mental health services: What the guidance says.* London: MIND publications. www.mind.org.uk/media/3352178/restraintguidanceweb.pdf

63.   Bowers, L. (2013, October). *The Safewards Model.* Retrieved 16 December 2016 from www.safewards.net/model/technical

64.   Carvel, J. (2004, 6 February). How the death of one black patient treated as a 'lesser being' showed up race bias. *The Guardian.* Retrieved 15 December 2016 from www.theguardian.com/uk/2004/feb/06/race.politics

65.   Blofeld, J. (2003). *An Independent Inquiry set up under HSG (94) 27 into the death of David 'Rocky' Bennett.* Cambridge: Norfolk, Suffolk and Cambridgeshire Strategic Health Authority.

66.   Monahan, J., Steadman, H., Silver, E., Appelbaum, P., Robbins, P., Mulvey, E. et al. (2001). *Rethinking risk assessment: The MacArthur Study of Mental Disorder and Violence.* Oxford: Oxford University Press.

67.   Papadopoulos, C., Ross, J., Stewart, D., Dack, C., James, K. & Bowers, L. (2012). The antecedents of violence and aggression within psychiatric in-patient settings. *Acta Psychiatrica Scandinavica, 125*(6), 425–439. http://onlinelibrary.wiley.com/doi/10.1111/j.1600-0447.2012.01827.x/pdf

68.   Health & Social Care Information Centre (2013, October 30). *Mental Health Act detentions top 50,000 a year.* Retrieved 21 May 2014 from www.hscic.gov.uk/3668

69.   Department of Health/National Statistics (2010). *In-patients formally detained in hospitals under the Mental Health Act 1983 and patients subject to supervised community treatment. Annual figures, England 2009/10.* London: Health and Social Care Information Centre, Community and Mental Health Team. www.hscic.gov.uk/catalogue/PUB12503/inp-det-m-h-a-1983-sup-com-eng-12-13-rep.pdf

70.   Audini, B. & Lelliott, P. (2002). Age, gender and ethnicity of those detained under Part II of the Mental Health Act 1983. *British Journal of Psychiatry, 180*, 222-226.

---

71.   Care Quality Commission. (2010). *Count me in 2010. Results of the 2010 national census of inpatients and patients on supervised community treatment in mental health and learning disability services in England and Wales.* London: Author.

72.   Mental Health Act Commission. (2009). *Coercion and consent: Monitoring the Mental Health Act 2007–2009. The Mental Health Act Commission Thirteenth Biennial Report 2007–2009.* London: Author. [Note: The MHAC's powers were transferred to the Care Quality Commission on 1 April 2009 and it then ceased operation]. www.cqc.org.uk/sites/default/files/documents/mhac_biennial_report_0709_final.pdf

73.   Burns, T., Rugkåsa, J., Molodynski, A., Dawson, J., Yeeles, K., Vazquez-Montes, M. et al. (2013, May 11). Community treatment orders for patients with psychosis (OCTET): A randomised controlled trial. *The Lancet, 381*(9878), 1627–1633. http://download.thelancet.com/pdfs/journals/lancet/PIIS0140673613601075.pdf?id=eaaolF3q BdvII9ohHqjKu

74.   British Psychological Society (1999). *Comments on the Review of the Mental Health Act 1983.* Leicester: British Psychological Society.

75.   Jarrett, M., Bowers, L. & Simpson, A. (2008). Coerced medication in psychiatric inpatient care: literature review. *Journal of Advanced Nursing, 64*(6), 538–548. http://onlinelibrary.wiley.com/doi/10.1111/j.1365-2648.2008.04832.x/pdf

76.   Katsakou, C. & Priebe, S. (2006). Outcomes of involuntary hospital admission: a review. *Acta Psychiatrica Scandinavica, 114*(4), 232–241. http://onlinelibrary.wiley.com/doi/10.1111/j.1600-0447.2006.00823.x/pdf

77.   Kisely, S., Campbell, L.A. & Preston, N. (2005). Compulsory community and involuntary outpatient treatment for people with severe mental disorders. *Cochrane Database Systematic Review, 3.* http://onlinelibrary.wiley.com/doi/10.1002/14651858.CD004408.pub3/pdf

78.   Loft, N. (2011). *Exploring compulsory admission experiences of adults with psychosis using grounded theory.* DClinPsych thesis. UK: Canterbury Christ Church University. http://create.canterbury.ac.uk/10433/1/Complete_MRP_-_Niki_Loft_-FINAL_LIBRARY_COPY.pdf

79.   Moncrieff, J., Cohen, D. & Mason, J. (2013). The patient's dilemma: An analysis of user's experiences of taking neuroleptic drugs. In S. Coles, S. Keenan & R. Diamond, *Madness contested: Power and practice.* Ross-on-Wye: PCCS Books.

80.   May, R. (2001, February 06). *Taking a stand.* (F. Keane, Interviewer) http://rufusmay.com/index.php?option=com_content&task=view&id=34&Itemid=29

81.   MIND (2015). *Restraint in mental health services: What the guidance says.* London: MIND publications. www.mind.org.uk/media/3352178/restraintguidanceweb.pdf

Section 11

1.   Kinderman, P. & Cooke, A. (2014, April 10). *A national scandal: psychological therapies for psychosis are helpful, but unavailable.* Retrieved 24 April 2014 from http://discursiveoftunbridgewells.blogspot.co.uk/2014/04/a-national-scandal- psychological.html

2.   Kazdin, A.E. (2009, July). Understanding how and why psychotherapy leads to change. *Psychotherapy Research, 19*(4–5), 418–428. www.tandfonline.com/doi/pdf/10.1080/10503300802448899

3.   Glover, G. & Evison, F. (2009). *Use of New Mental Health Services by Ethnic Minorities in England.* Stockton-on-Tees: North East Public Health Observatory.

4.   MIND (2013). *We still need to talk: A report on accessing talking therapies.* London: MIND publications. www.mind.org.uk/media/494424/we-still-need-to-talk_report.pdf

5.   Morrison, A.P., Turkington, D., Pyle, M., Spencer, H., Brabban, A., Dunn, G. et al. (2014). Cognitive therapy for people with schizophrenia spectrum disorders not taking antipsychotic drugs: a single-blind randomised trial. *The Lancet, 383*(9926), 1395-1403. http://download. thelancet.com/pdfs/journals/lancet/PIIS0140673613622461.pdf?id=eaaolF3q BdvII9ohHqjKu

6.   Morrison, A.P., Hutton, P., Shiers, D. & Turkington, D. (2012). Antipsychotics: is it time to introduce patient choice? *British Journal of Psychiatry, 201,* 83–84. http://bjp.rcpsych.org/ content/201/2/83.full.pdf+html

7.   Morrison, A., Wardle, M., Hutton, P., Davies, L., Dunn, G., Brabban, A. et al. (2013). Assessing cognitive therapy instead of neuroleptics: Rationale, study design and sample characteristics of the ACTION trial. *Psychosis: Psychological, Social and Integrative Approaches, 5*(1), 82–92. www.tandfonline.com/doi/pdf/10.1080/17522439.2012.756539

8.   Morrison, A., Hutton, P., Wardle, M., Spencer, H., Barratt, S., Brabban, A. et al. (2012). Cognitive therapy for people with a schizophrenia spectrum diagnosis not taking antipsychotic medication: an exploratory trial. *Psychological Medicine, 42*(5), 1049-1056. www.thelancet.com/journals/lancet/article/PIIS0140-6736(13)62246-1/abstract

9.   Chadwick, P.K. (2006). *Person-based cognitive therapy for distressing voices.* Chichester: Wiley.

10. Rogers, C.R. (2004). *On becoming a person* (new edn.). London: Constable.

11. Chadwick, P.K. (2006). *Person-based cognitive therapy for distressing voices.* Chichester: Wiley.

12. Morrison, A.P., Renton, J.P., French, P. & Bentall, R.P. (2007) *Think you're crazy? Think again: A resource book for cognitive therapy for psychosis.* London: Routledge www.amazon.co.uk/Think-Youre-Crazy-Again- Cognitive/dp/158391837X/ ref=sr_1_1?s=books&ie=UTF8&qid=1402070646&sr=1-1

13. Freeman, D. & Garety, P. (2006). Helping patients with paranoid and suspicious thoughts. *Advances in Psychiatric Treatment, 12,* 404–415. http://apt.rcpsych.org/content/12/6/404.full

14. Morrison, A.P., Haddock, G. & Tarrier, N. (1995). Intrusive thoughts and auditory hallucinations: a cognitive approach. *Behavioural and Cognitive Psychotherapy, 23,* 265–280. http://journals.cambridge.org/action/displayFulltext?type=1&fid=5091216&jid=BCP&

15. Greenwood, K., Sweeney, A., Williams, S., Garety, P., Kuipers, E., Scott, J. et al. (2010). CHoice of Outcome In Cbt for psychosEs (CHOICE): The development of a new service user–led outcome measure of CBT for psychosis. *Schizophrenia Bulletin, 36*(1), 126–135. http://tinyurl.com/pbxlltf

16. Garety, P.A. & Freeman, D. (2013). The past and future of delusions research: from the inexplicable to the treatable. *British Journal of Psychiatry, 203*(5), 327–333. http://bjp.rcpsych.org/content/203/5/327.full.pdf+html

17.   Wykes, T. (in press). Cognitive behaviour therapy and schizophrenia. *Evidence-Based Mental Health.*

18.   Sen, D. (2002). *The world is full of laughter.* Brentwood: Chipmunka Publishing.

19.   Wykes, T., Steel, C., Everitt, B. & Tarrier, N. (2008). Cognitive behavior therapy for schizophrenia: Effect sizes, clinical models, and methodological rigor. *Schizophrenia Bulletin, 34*(3), 523-537. http://schizophreniabulletin.oxfordjournals.org/content/34/3/523.full

20.   van der Gaag, M., Valmaggia, L.R. & Smit, F. (2014, June). The effects of individually tailored formulation-based cognitive behavioural therapy in auditory hallucinations and delusions: A meta-analysis. *Schizophrenia Research, 156*(1), 30-37. http://www.sciencedirect.com/science/article/pii/S0920996414001340

21.   Pfammatter, M., Junghan, U.M., & Brenner, H.D. (2006). Efficacy of psychological therapy in schizophrenia: Conclusions from meta-analyses. *Schizophrenia Bulletin, 32*(1), S64-S80. www.ncbi.nlm.nih.gov/pmc/articles/PMC2632545/pdf/sbl030.pdf

22.   Wykes, T., Steel, C., Everitt, B. & Tarrier, N. (2008, May). Cognitive behavior therapy for schizophrenia: Effect sizes, clinical models, and methodological rigor. *Schizophrenia Bulletin, 34*(3), 523-537. http://schizophreniabulletin.oxfordjournals.org/content/34/3/523.full

23.   Turner, D.T., van der Gaag, M., Karyotaki, E. & Cuijpers, P. (2014, May). Psychological interventions for psychosis: a meta-analysis of comparative outcome studies. *American Journal of Psychiatry, 171*(5), 523–538. http://journals.psychiatryonline.org/article.aspx?volume=171&page=523

24.   National Institute for Health and Care Excellence (2014). *Psychosis and schizophrenia in adults: treatment and management. NICE clinical guidelines.* London: National Institute for Health and Care Excellence. www.nice.org.uk/nicemedia/live/14382/66534/66534.pdf

25.   Correll, C.U. & Carbon, M. (2014). Efficacy of pharmacologic and psychotherapeutic interventions in psychiatry: To talk or to prescribe: Is that the question? *JAMA Psychiatry, 71*(6), 624–626. http://archpsyc.jamanetwork.com/article.aspx?articleid=1865001

26.   Burns, A.M., Erickson, D.H. & Brenner, C.A. (2014, April 1). Cognitive-behavioral therapy for medication-resistant psychosis: a meta-analytic review. *Psychiatric Services.* http://ps.psychiatryonline.org/article.aspx?articleID=1857288

27.   Berry, C. & Hayward, M. (2011, July). What can qualitative research tell us about service user perspectives of CBT for psychosis? A synthesis of current evidence. *Behavioural and Cognitive Psychotherapy, 39*(4), 487–494. www.ncbi.nlm.nih.gov/pubmed/21457606

28.   Kumari, V., Fannon, D., Peters, E.R., Ffytche, D.H., Sumich, A.L., Premkumar, P. et al. (2011). Neural changes following cognitive behaviour therapy for psychosis: a longitudinal study. *Brain: a journal of neurology, 134*(8), 2396–2407 http://brain.oxfordjournals.org/content/134/8/2396.full.pdf+html

29.   National Institute for Health and Care Excellence (2014). *Psychosis and schizophrenia in adults: treatment and management. NICE clinical guidelines.* London: National Institute for Health and Care Excellence. www.nice.org.uk/nicemedia/live/14382/66534/66534.pdf

30. Schizophrenia Commission (2012). *The abandoned illness: A report from the Schizophrenia Commission.* London: Rethink Mental Illness: www.rethink.org/media/514093/TSC_main_ report_14_nov.pdf

31. Kinderman, P. & Cooke, A. (2014, April 10). *A national scandal: psychological therapies for psychosis are helpful, but unavailable.* Retrieved 24 April 2014 from http:// discursiveoftunbridgewells.blogspot.co.uk/2014/04/

32. Roth, A.D. & Pilling, S. (2013). *Competence framework for psychological interventions for people with psychosis and bipolar disorder.* Retrieved 7 March 2014 from www.ucl. ac.uk/clinical-psychology/CORE/Docs/web%20competences% 20psychosis%20and%20 bipolar/Background%20document/Working%20with%20Psychosis% 20and%20Bipolar%20 Disorder%20background%20document%20web%20version.pdf

33. Morrison, A.P. & Barratt, S. (2010). What are the components of CBT for psychosis? A Delphi study. *Schizophrenia Bulletin, 36*(1), 136–42. www.ncbi.nlm.nih.gov/pmc/articles/ PMC2800146/

34. Kilbride, Martina et al (2013) Exploring service users' perceptions of cognitive behavioural therapy for psychosis: A user led study. *Behavioural and Cognitive Psychotherapy, 44*(1), 89–102. http://journals.cambridge. org/action/displayAbstract?fromPage=online&aid=8768845&fulltex tType=RA&fileId=S1352465812000495

35. Waller, H., Garety, P.A., Jolley, S., Fornells-Ambrojo, M., Kuipers, E., Onwumere, J. et al. (2013, March). Low intensity cognitive behavioural therapy for psychosis: a pilot study. *Journal of Behavioural Therapy & Experimental Psychiatry, 44*(2), 98–104. www.ncbi.nlm.nih.gov/ pubmed/22940787

36. Tarrier, N., Harwood, S., Yusopoff, L., Beckett, R. & Baker, A. (1990). Coping strategy enhancement (CSE): A method of treating residual schizophrenic symptoms. *Behavioural Psychotherapy, 18*(4), 283–293. http://journals.cambridge.org/action/ displayAbstract?fromPage=online&aid=5852460

37. Hogg, L.I. (1996). Psychological treatments for negative symptoms. In G. Haddock & P. Slade, *Cognitive-behavioural interventions with psychotic disorders* (pp.151–170). London: Routledge.

38. Myers, E., Startup, H. & Freeman, D. (2011). Cognitive behavioural treatment of insomnia in individuals with persistent persecutory delusions: A pilot trial. *Journal of Behaviour Therapy and Experimental Psychiatry, 42*(3), 330–336. www.sciencedirect.com/science/article/pii/ S0005791611000279

39. Freeman, D., Stahl, D., McManus, S., Meltzer, H., Brufha, T., Wiles, N. et al. (2012). Insomnia, worry, anxiety and depression as predictors of the occurrence and persistence of paranoid thinking. *Social Psychiatry and Psychiatric Epidemiology, 47*, 1195–1203. http://link.springer. com/article/10.1007/s00127-011-0433-1#page-1

40. Bell, M., Bryson, G. & Wexler, B.E. (2003). Cognitive remediation of working memory deficits: durability of training effects in severely impaired and less severely impaired schizophrenia. *Acta Psychiatrica Scandinavica, 108*, 101–109. http://onlinelibrary.wiley.com/doi/10.1034/ j.1600-0447.2003.00090.x/pdf

41.   McGurk, S.R., Twamley, E.W., Sitzer, D.I., McHugo, G.J. & Mueser, K.T. (2007). A meta-analysis of cognitive remediation in schizophrenia. *American Journal of Psychiatry, 164*, 1791–1802. http://ajp.psychiatryonline.org/data/Journals/AJP/3842/07aj1791.PDF

42.   Drake, R.J., Day, C.J., Picucci, R., Warburton, J., Larkin, W., Husain, N. et al. (2014). A naturalistic, randomized, controlled trial combining cognitive remediation with cognitive–behavioural therapy after first-episode non-affective psychosis. *Psychological Medicine, 44*, 1889–1899 http://journals.cambridge.org/download.php?file=%2FPSM%2FPSM44_09%2FS00332917130 02559a.pdf&tcode=f14093dedf029a6b2cf84720c13bb8d5

43.   Read, J., Fosse, R., Moskowitz, A. & Perry, B. (2014, February). The traumagenic neurodevelopmental model of psychosis revisited. *Neuropsychiatry, 4*(1), 65–79. www.futuremedicine.com/doi/full/10.2217/npy.13.89

44.   Larkin, W. & Morrison, A.P. (2006). *Trauma and psychosis: New directions for theory and therapy.* Hove: Routledge.

45.   Herman, J. (1992). *Trauma and recovery: The aftermath of violence – from domestic abuse to political terror.* New York: Basic Books.

46.   Ross, C.A. & Halpern, N. (2009). *Trauma model therapy: A treatment approach for trauma, dissociation and complex comorbidity.* Richardson, TX: Manitou Communications Inc.

47.   Boon, S., Steele, K. & Van Der Hart, O. (2011). *Coping with trauma-related dissociation: Skills training for patients and therapists.* New York: W.W. Norton & Company.

48.   Dillon, J. (2008). *The tale of an ordinary little girl.* Retrieved 12 November 2013 from www.jacquidillon.org/biography/background

49.   Chadwick, P., Hughes, S., Russell, D., Russell, I. & Dagnan, D. (2009). Mindfulness groups for distressing voices and paranoia: a replication and randomized feasibility trial. *Behavioural and Cognitive Psychotherapy, 37*(4), 403–412. www.bangor.ac.uk/mindfulness/documents/StephanieHughes.pdf

50.   Morris, E.M.J., Johns, L.C. & Oliver, J.E. (2013). *Acceptance and commitment therapy and mindfulness for psychosis.* London: Wiley-Blackwell.

51.   Bach, P.A., Guadiano, B., Pankey, J., Herbert, J.D. & Hayes, S.C. (2006). Acceptance, mindfulness, values and psychosis: Applying acceptance and commitment therapy (ACT) to the chronically mental ill. In R.A. Baer (Ed.), *Mindfulness-based treatment approaches: Clinicians guide to evidence base and applications* (pp.93–116). San Diego, CA: Elsevier Academic Press.

52.   Oliver, J., Joseph, C., Byrne, M., Johns, L. & Morris, E. (2013). Introduction to mindfulness and acceptance based therapies for psychosis. In J.E. Oliver, *Acceptance and commitment therapy and mindfulness for psychosis* (pp.1–11). London: Wiley-Blackwell.

53.   Rhodes, J. & Jacques, S. (2009). *Narrative CBT for psychosis.* London: Routledge.

54.   White, M. (1987). *Family therapy and schizophrenia: Addressing the 'in-the-corner' lifestyle.* Adelaide: Dulwich Centre Publications.

55. White, M. (2013, Feb 15). *Insider knowledge on coping with voices and visions.* Retrieved 11 November 2013 from http://shrinkrants.tumblr.com/post/43147469717/insider-knowledge-on-coping-with-voices-and-visions

56. Corstens, D., May, R. & Longden, E. (2011). *Talking with voices.* Retrieved 7 June 2014 from http://rufusmay.com/index.php?option=com_content&task=view&id=94&Itemid=9

57. May, R. (2013, June 9). *Avatar therapy – a new battle for the tree of life.* Retrieved 22 September 2014 from www.madinamerica.com/2013/06/avatar-therapy-a-new-battle-for-the-tree-of-life/

58. Kuipers, E. (2011) Cognitive behavioural therapy and family intervention for psychosis – evidence-based but unavailable? The next steps. *Psychoanalytic Psychotherapy, 25*(1),69–74. www.brown.uk.com/schizophrenia/kuipers2.pdf

59. Meddings, S., Gordon, I. & Owen, D. (2010). Family and systemic work. In C. Cuppitt (Ed.), *Reaching out: The psychology of Assertive Outreach.* London, UK: Routledge.

60. Rethink. (2010). *Fair treatment now: Better outcomes, lower costs in severe mental illness.* London: Rethink. www.psychminded.co.uk/news/news2010/july10/Rethink-fair-treatment- now.pdf

61. Pharoah, F., Rathbone, J. & Wong, W. (2010). Family intervention for schizophrenia (Review). *Cochrane Collaboration.* John Wiley & Sons. http://onlinelibrary.wiley.com/doi/10.1002/14651858.CD000088.pub3/pdf/standard

62. National Institute for Health and Care Excellence (2014). *Psychosis and schizophrenia in adults: treatment and management. NICE clinical guidelines.* London: National Institute for Health and Care Excellence. www.nice.org.uk/nicemedia/live/14382/66534/66534.pdf

63. National Institute for Health and Care Excellence (2014). *Psychosis and schizophrenia in adults: treatment and management. NICE clinical guidelines.* London: National Institute for Health and Care Excellence. www.nice.org.uk/nicemedia/live/14382/66534/66534.pdf

64. Sen, D. (2013, February 14). *Maudsley Hospital pioneers mental health therapy scheme.* (E. Wickham, Interviewer) ITV. www.itv.com/news/london/update/2012-12-20/maudsley-hospital-pioneers-mental-health-therapy-scheme/

65. National Institute for Health and Care Excellence (2014). *Psychosis and schizophrenia in adults: treatment and management. NICE clinical guidelines.* London: National Institute for Health and Care Excellence. www.nice.org.uk/nicemedia/live/14382/66534/66534.pdf

66. Schizophrenia Commission. (2012). *The abandoned illness: A report from the Schizophrenia Commission.* London: Rethink Mental Illness. www.rethink.org/media/514093/TSC_main_report_14_nov.pdf

67. MIND (November 2013). *We still need to talk: A report on access to talking therapies.* London: MIND. www.rethink.org/media/869903/We_still_need_to_talk.pdf

68. Improving Access to Psychological Therapies (2013, Mar 07). *Severe mental illness.* Retrieved Dec 06, 2013 from www.iapt.nhs.uk/smi-/

69. Gould, M. (2011, January 28). *When it comes to better mental health, it really can be good to talk.* Retrieved 19 June 2014 from www.thetimes.co.uk/tto/business/industries/publicsector/article2891461.ece

70. Jarrett, C. (2008, January). When therapy causes harm. *The Psychologist, 21*(1), 10–12. www.thepsychologist.org.uk/archive/archive_home.cfm?volumeID=21&editionID=155&Article ID=1290

71. Glover, G. & Evison, F. (2009). *Use of new mental health services by ethnic minorities in England.* Durham: North East Public Health Observatory.

72. Kalathil, J. (2011). *Recovery and Resilience: African, African-Caribbean and South Asian women's narratives of recovering from mental distress.* Retrieved 1 December 2016 from www.mentalhealth.org.uk/publications/recovery-and-resilience/

73. Kalathil, J. (2011). *Recovery and Resilience: African, African-Caribbean and South Asian women's narratives of recovering from mental distress.* Retrieved 1 December 2016 from www.mentalhealth.org.uk/publications/recovery-and-resilience/

74. Kim, U., Yang, K.S., & Hwang, K.K. (Eds.). (2006). *Indigenous and cultural psychology: Understanding people in context.* New York: Springer Science & Business Media.

75. Sue, D.W. & Sue, D. (2012). *Counseling the culturally diverse: Theory and practice.* Hoboken, NJ: Wiley.

76. Schizophrenia Commission (2012). *The abandoned illness: A report from the Schizophrenia Commission.* London: Rethink Mental Illness. www.rethink.org/media/514093/TSC_main_ report_14_nov.pdf

77. Hutton, P., Morrison, A.P. & Taylor, H. (2012). Brief cognitive behavioural therapy for hallucinations: Can it help people who decide not to take antipsychotic medication? A case study. *Behavioural Cognitive Psychotherapy, 40*(1), 111–116 http://journals.cambridge.org/ action/displayAbstract?fromPage=online&taid=8445959

Section 12

1. Wunderink, M., Nieboer, R.M., Wiersma, D., Sytema, S. & Nienhuis, F. J. (2013, September). Recovery in remitted first-episode psychosis at 7 years of follow-up of an early dose reduction/discontinuation or maintenance treatment strategy: long-term follow-up of a 2- year randomized clinical trial. *JAMA Psychiatry, 70*(9). http://archpsyc.jamanetwork.com/ article.aspx?articleid=1707650

2. Kapur, S. & Mamo, D. (2003, October). Half a century of antipsychotics and still a central role for dopamine D2 receptors. *Progress in Neuro-Psychopharmacology and Biological Psychiatry, 27*(7), 1081–1090. www.sciencedirect.com/science/article/pii/S0278584603002173

3. Moncrieff, J. (2007). *The myth of the chemical cure.* Palgrave Macmillan.

4. Mizrahi, R., Kiang, M., Mamo, D.C., Arenovich, T., Bagby, R.M., Zipursky, R.B. et al. (2006, December). The selective effect of antipsychotics on the different dimensions of the experience of psychosis in schizophrenia spectrum disorders. *Schizophrenia Research, 88*(1–3), 111–118. www.sciencedirect.com/science/article/pii/S0920996406003161

5. Moncrieff, J. (2007). *The myth of the chemical cure.* Palgrave Macmillan.

6. Moncrieff, J. (2007). *The myth of the chemical cure.* Palgrave Macmillan.

7. Chadwick, P. K. (1997). *Schizophrenia: The positive perspective.* London: Routledge.

8. Chadwick, P.K. (2007, January). Peer-professional first-person account: Schizophrenia from the inside – phenomenology and the integration of causes and meanings. *Schizophrenia Bulletin, 33*(1), 166–173. www.ncbi.nlm.nih.gov/pmc/articles/PMC2632294/pdf/sbl034.pdf

9. Slade, M. (2009). *Personal recovery and mental illness,* p.174. Cambridge: Cambridge University Press.

10. Watkins, P. (2007). *Recovery: A guide for mental health practitioners.* London: Elsevier.

11. Sen, D. (2002). T*he world is full of laughter.* Brentwood: Chipmunka Publishing.

12. Morken, G., Widen, J.H. & Grawe, R.W. (2008, April 30). Non-adherence to antipsychotic medication, relapse and rehospitalisation in recent-onset schizophrenia. *BMC Psychiatry, 8*(32). www.ncbi.nlm.nih.gov/pmc/articles/PMC2390550/pdf/1471-244X-8-32.pdf

13. Morrison, A.P., Hutton, P., Shiers, D. & Turkington, D. (2012). Antipsychotics: is it time to introduce patient choice? *British Journal of Psychiatry, 201,* 83–84. http://bjp.rcpsych.org/content/201/2/83.short

14. National Institute for Health and Care Excellence (2014). *Psychosis and schizophrenia in adults: treatment and management. NICE clinical guidelines.* London: National Institute for Health and Care Excellence. www.nice.org.uk/nicemedia/live/14382/66534/66534.pdf

15. Harrow, M., Jobe, T.H. & Faull, R.N. (2012). Do all schizophrenia patients need antipsychotic treatment continuously throughout their lifetime? A 20-year longitudinal study. *Psychological Medicine, 42*(10), 2145–2155. www.ncbi.nlm.nih.gov/pubmed/22340278

16. Wunderink, M., Nieboer, R.M., Wiersma, D., Sytema, S. & Nienhuis, F.J. (2013, September). Recovery in remitted first-episode psychosis at 7 years of follow-up of an early dose reduction/discontinuation or maintenance treatment strategy: long-term follow-up of a 2- year randomized clinical trial. *JAMA Psychiatry, 70*(9). http://archpsyc.jamanetwork.com/article.aspx?articleid=1707650

17. Healy, D. (2012, August). *Richard B goes mad.* Retrieved 20 June 2013 from http://davidhealy.org/wp-content/uploads/2012/08/Richard-B-goes-Mad.pdf

18. Jones Edward, G. (2012, August). *An eye opener (antipsychotics – adverse effects).* Retrieved 20 June 2013 from http://davidhealy.org/wp-content/uploads/2012/08/Gwen-Eye-opener-Phil-Thomas.pdf

19. Moncrieff, J., Cohen, D. & Mason, J.P. (2009). The subjective experience of taking antipsychotic medication: a content analysis of internet data. *Acta Psychiatrica Scandinavia, 120,* 102–111. www.mentalhealth.freeuk.com/acta.pdf

20. Leucht, S., Cipriani, A., Spineli, L., Mavridis, D., Orey, D., Richter, F. et al. (2013, September 14). Comparative efficacy and tolerability of 15 antipsychotic drugs in schizophrenia: a multiple-treatments meta-analysis. *The Lancet, 382*(9896), 951–962. www.doctorsonly.co.il/wp-content/uploads/2013/10/22102013_psych_Leucht.pdf

21. Chadwick, P.K. (1997). *Schizophrenia: The positive perspective.* London: Routledge.

22. Moncrieff, J. (2013, December 13). *Antipsychotics and brain shrinkage: an update.* Retrieved 6 January 2014 from http://joannamoncrieff.com/2013/12/13/antipsychotics-and-brain-shrinkage-an-update/

23. Morrison, A.P., Hutton, P., Shiers, D. & Turkington, D. (2012). Antipsychotics: is it time to introduce patient choice? *British Journal of Psychiatry, 201*, 83–84. http://bjp.rcpsych.org/content/201/2/83.short

24. Andreasen, N.C., Liu, D., Ziebell, S., Vora, A. & Ho, B.-C. (2013, June). Relapse duration, treatment intensity, and brain tissue loss in schizophrenia: a prospective longitudinal MRI study. *American Journal of Psychiatry, 170*, 609–615. http://ajp.psychiatryonline.org/article.aspx?articleid=1676090

25. Whitaker, R. (2010). *Anatomy of an epidemic: Magic bullets, psychiatric drugs, and the astonishing rise of mental illness in America.* New York: Crown.

26. Tiihonen, J., Lönnqvist, J., Wahlbeck, K., Klaukka, T., Niskanen, L., Tanskanen, A. et al. (2009, August 22). 11-year follow-up of mortality in patients with schizophrenia: a population-based cohort study (FIN11 study). *The Lancet, 374*(9690), 620–627. http://www.sciencedirect.com/science/article/pii/S014067360960742X?np=y

27. Tiihonen, J., Lönnqvist, J., Wahlbeck, K., Klaukka, T., Niskanen, L., Tanskanen, A. et al. (2009, August 22). 11-year follow-up of mortality in patients with schizophrenia: a population-based cohort study (FIN11 study). *The Lancet, 374*(9690), 620–627. http://www.sciencedirect.com/science/article/pii/S014067360960742X?np=y

28. Whitaker, R. (2002). *Mad in America.* Cambridge, MA: Perseus Publishing.

29. Whitaker, R. (2010). *Anatomy of an epidemic: Magic bullets, psychiatric drugs, and the astonishing rise of mental illness in America.* New York: Crown.

30. Cromby, J., Harper, D. & Reavey, P. (2013). *Psychology, mental health and distress.* London: Palgrave Macmillan.

31. Faulkner, A. (1997). *Knowing our own minds: Users views of alternative and complementary treatments in mental health.* London: Mental Health Foundation.

32. Collis, H. (2013, July 06). *'Medication makes me feel like a zombie': Frank Bruno's torment as he begs to come off drugs for his mental illness.* Retrieved 6 December 2013 from www.dailymail.co.uk/news/article-2357261/Medication-makes-feel-like-zombie-Frank-Brunos-torment-begs-come-drugs-mental-illness.html#ixzz2a45puXEc

33. Westcott, P. (1979, April 14). One man's schizophrenic illness. *British Medical Journal, 1*, 989–990. www.ncbi.nlm.nih.gov/pmc/articles/PMC1598693/pdf/brmedj00068-0023.pdf

34. Nicol, A. (2011). My dialogue with diagnosis. In A. Grant, F. Biley & H. Walker (Eds.), *Our encounters with madness.* Ross-on-Wye: PCCS Books.

35. Morrison, A.P., Hutton, P., Shiers, D. & Turkington, D. (2012). Antipsychotics: is it time to introduce patient choice? *British Journal of Psychiatry, 201*, 83–84. http://bjp.rcpsych.org/content/201/2/83.full.pdf+html

36. Coming Off (2014). *Introducing the Coming Off Psychiatric Meds website.* Retrieved 22 May 2014 from www.comingoff.com/index.php?option=com_frontpage&Itemid=1

37. MIND (2014). *Coming off psychiatric drugs.* Retrieved 22 May 2014 from Mind for better mental health: www.mind.org.uk/information-support/drugs-and-treatments/medication-stopping-or-coming-off/

38. National Institute for Health and Care Excellence (2014). *Psychosis and schizophrenia in adults: treatment and management. NICE clinical guidelines.* London: National Institute for Health and Care Excellence. www.nice.org.uk/nicemedia/live/14382/66534/66534.pdf

39. Morken, G., Widen, J.H. & Grawe, R.W. (2008, April 30). Non-adherence to antipsychotic medication, relapse and rehospitalisation in recent-onset schizophrenia. *BMC Psychiatry, 8*(32). www.ncbi.nlm.nih.gov/pmc/articles/PMC2390550/pdf/1471-244X-8-32.pdf

40. Romme, M. & Escher, S. (1993). *Accepting voices,* p.55. London: MIND.

41. May, R. (2000). Routes to recovery from psychosis: The routes of a clinical psychologist. *Clinical Psychology Forum, 146,* 6–10.

42. Royal College of Psychiatrists (2006). *Consensus statement on the use of high dose antipsychotic medication (No. CR138).* Royal College of Psychiatrists. www.rcpsych.ac.uk/files/pdfversion/cr138.pdf

43. Royal College of Psychiatrists (2006). *Consensus statement on the use of high dose antipsychotic medication (No. CR138).* Royal College of Psychiatrists. www.rcpsych.ac.uk/files/pdfversion/cr138.pdf

44. National Institute for Health and Care Excellence (2014). *Psychosis and schizophrenia in adults: treatment and management. NICE clinical guidelines.* London: National Institute for Health and Care Excellence. www.nice.org.uk/nicemedia/live/14382/66534/66534.pdf

45. Royal College of Psychiatrists (2013). *What is POMH-UK?* Retrieved 11 November 2013 from www.rcpsych.ac.uk/workinpsychiatry/qualityimprovement/ nationalclinicalaudits/ prescribingpomh/prescribingobservatorypomh.aspx

Part 4

Section 13

1. Centre for Mental Health and Mental Health Network NHS Confederation (2014). *Recovery is just the start.* Retrieved 7 March 2014 from Implementing Recovery through Organisational Change (ImROC): www.imroc.org/

2. Dillon, J. (2008). *The tale of an ordinary little girl.* Retrieved 12 November 2013 from www.jacquidillon.org/biography/background

3. Johnstone, L. (2013, September 13). *Using psychological formulation in teams.* Retrieved 22 May 2014 from http://dxsummit.org/archives/1306

4. Johnstone, L. & Dallos, R. (2013). *Formulation in psychology and psychotherapy: Making sense of people's problems.* Hove: Routledge.

5. Perkins, R. & Repper, J. (1998). *Dilemmas in community mental health practice: Choice or control.* Abingdon: Radcliffe Medical Press.

6. Herz, M.I., Glazer, W.M., Mostert, M.A., Sheard, M.A., Szymanski, H.V., Hafez, H. et al. (1991). Intermittent vs maintenance medication in schizophrenia. Two year results. *Archives of General Psychiatry, 48*(4), 333–339. www.ncbi.nlm.nih.gov/pubmed/1672588

7. Coleman, R. (2014). *Working to Recovery Ltd.* Retrieved 12 February 2014 from www.workingtorecovery.co.uk/ron-coleman

8. Chadwick, P.K. (1997). *Schizophrenia: The positive perspective.* London: Routledge.

9. Campbell, P. (1996). Challenging loss of power. In J. Reads & J. Reynolds, *Speaking our minds* (pp.56-62). Milton Keynes: Open University Press.

10. Dace, E., Faulkner, A., Frost, M., Parker, K., Pembroke, L. & Smith, A. (1998). *The 'Hurt Yourself Less' Workbook.* Retrieved 21 June 2013 from www.kreativeinterventions.com/TheHurtYourselfLessWorkbook.pdf

11. Oquosa, O. (2012). Cultural ignorance and psychiatric labeling [Online testimony]. Inquiry into the 'Schizophrenia' Label. Retrieved 20 December 2016 from http://www.schizophreniainquiry.org/testimonies?page=4

12. Carr, A. (2004). *Positive psychology: The science of happiness and human strengths.* Brunner-Routledge.

13. National Institute for Health and Clinical Excellence (2011). *Service user experience in adult mental health: improving the experience of care for people using adult NHS mental health services.* London: NICE.

14. South West London and St George's Mental Health NHS Trust (2000, February). *Charter for the employment of people who have experienced mental health problems.* Retrieved 11 November 2013 from www.swlstg-tr.nhs.uk/work-for- us/service_user_employment_programme/charter_for_the_employment_of_people_who_have_experienced_mental_health_problems/

15. Mednet Consult Ltd. (2011). *The cluster pathway guide.* Retrieved 12 November 2013 from www.mednetconsult.co.uk

16. Johnstone, L. & Dallos, R. (2013). *Formulation in psychology and psychotherapy.* Hove: Routledge.

17. Schizophrenia Commission. (2012). *The abandoned illness: A report from the Schizophrenia Commission.* London: Rethink Mental Illness. www.rethink.org/media/514093/TSC_main_report_14_nov.pdf

18. Glover, G. & Evison, F. (2009). *Use of new mental health services by ethnic minorities in England.* Durham: North East Public Health Observatory.

19. MIND (2013). *We still need to talk: A report on accessing talking therapies.* London: MIND publications. www.mind.org.uk/media/494424/we-still-need-to-talk_report.pdf

20. Naeem, F., Phiri, P., Rathod, S. & Kingdon, D. (2010). Using CBT with diverse patients: Working with South Asian Muslims. In M. Mueller, H. Kennerley, F. McManus & D. Westbrook (Eds.) *Oxford guide to surviving as a CBT therapist* (pp.41–55). Oxford: Oxford University Press.

21. Rathod, S., Kingdon, D., Phiri, P. & Gobbi, M. (2010). Developing culturally sensitive cognitive behaviour therapy for psychosis for ethnic minority patients by exploration and incorporation of service users' and health professionals' views and opinions. *Behavioural and Cognitive Psychotherapy, 38*(5), 511–533. www.brown.uk.com/schizophrenia/rathod.pdf

22. Rathod, S., Phiri, P., Harris, S., Underwood, C., et al. (2013). Cognitive behaviour therapy for psychosis can be adapted for minority ethnic groups: A randomised controlled trial. *Schizophrenia Research, 143*(2), 319-326.

23. Byrne, A., Warren, A., Joof, B., Johnson, D., et al. (2011). 'A powerful piece of work': African Caribbean men talking about the 'tree of life'. *Context: A magazine for family therapy and systemic practice, 117*, 40–45.

24. Denborough, D. (2008). *Collective narrative practice: Responding to individuals, groups and communities who have experienced trauma.* Adelaide: Dulwich Centre.

25. Moodley, R. & West, W. (2005). *Integrating traditional healing practices into counselling and psychotherapy.* Thousand Oaks, London and New Delhi: Sage.

26. Sutherland, P., Moodley, R. & Chevannes, B. (2014). *Caribbean Healing Traditions. Implications for health and mental health.* New York and London: Routledge.

27. Seebohm, P., Henderson, P., Munn-Giddings, C., Thomas, P. & Yasmeen, S. (2005). *Together we will change: Community development, mental health and diversity – Learning from challenge and achievement at Sharing Voices (Bradford).* London: The Sainsbury Centre for Mental Health.

28. Kalathil, J. (2011). *Dancing to our own tunes: Reassessing black and minority ethnic mental health service user involvement.* London: Afiya Trust/National Service User Network. Retrieved 20 December 2016 from www.nsun.org.uk/assets/downloadableFiles/dtoots_report_reprint-oct-20112.pdf

29. Begum, N. (2006). *Doing it for themselves: Participation and black and minority ethnic service users.* London: Social Care Institute for Excellence. Retrieved 20 December 2016 from www.scie.org.uk/publications/reports/report14.pdf

30. Newnes, C. (1993). Editorial. *Clinical Psychology Forum, 54*(2).

31. National Institute for Health and Clinical Excellence (2011). *Information for people who use NHS mental health services*. Manchester: NICE. www.nice.org.uk/nicemedia/live/13846/60327/60327.pdf

32. Meyer, H., Taiminen, T., Vuori, T., Äijälä, A., & Helenius, H. (1999). Posttraumatic stress disorder symptoms related to psychosis and acute involuntary hospitalization in schizophrenic and delusional patients. *The Journal of Nervous and Mental Disease, 187*(6), 343–352.

33. Morrison, A. P., Frame, L., & Larkin, W. (2003). Relationships between trauma and psychosis: A review and integration. *British Journal of Clinical Psychology, 42*(4), 331–353.

34. Macpherson, W. (1999). *The Stephen Lawrence inquiry report*. London: Author. Retrieved 20 December 2016 from www.gov.uk/government/uploads/system/uploads/attachment_data/file/277111/4262.pdf

35. Keating, F. & Robertson, D. (2004). Fear, black people and mental illness: A vicious circle? *Health and Social Care in the Community, 12*(5), 439-447.

36. Keating, F., Robertson, D., McCulloch, A. & Francis, E. (2003). *Breaking the circles of fear: A review of the relationship between mental health services and African and Caribbean communities*. London: The Sainsbury Centre for Mental Health. Retrieved 20 December 2016 from www.offtherecordcroydon.org/media/4901/breaking_the_circles_of_fear.pdf

37. Salway, S.M., Mir, G., Turner, D., Ellison, G.T.H, Carter, L, & Gerrish, K. (2016). Obstacles to 'race equality' in the English National Health Service: Insights from the healthcare commissioning arena. *Social Science & Medicine, 152*, 102–110. Retrieved 20 December 2016 from www.sciencedirect.com/science/article/pii/S0277953616300326

38. Méndez, J.E. (2013, March 08). *UN Rapporteur on Torture calls for ban on forced treatment*. Retrieved 7 March 2014 from www.madinamerica.com/2013/03/u-n-rapporteur-on-torture-calls-for-ban-on-forced-treatment/

39. Rufus May. (2010). In S. Jones, F. Lobban & A. Cooke. (2010). *Understanding bipolar disorder: Why some people experience extreme mood states and what can help*, p.57. Leicester: British Psychological Society.

40. Cole, E.R. (2009). Intersectionality and research in psychology. *American Psychologist, 64*(3), 170. www.brown.uk.com/brownlibrary/DJH.htm

41. Phoenix, A. & Pattynama, P. (2006). Intersectionality. *European Journal of Women's Studies, 13*(3), 187-192. https://hal.archives-ouvertes.fr/hal-00571273/document

42. Rosenthal, L. (2016). Incorporating intersectionality into psychology: An opportunity to promote social justice and equity. *American Psychologist, 71*(6), 474-485.

43. Blofeld, J. (2003). An Independent Inquiry set up under HSG (94) 27 into the death of David 'Rocky' Bennett. Cambridge: Norfolk, Suffolk and Cambridgeshire Strategic Health Authority.

44. Department of Health. (2005). *Delivering race equality in mental health care: An action plan for reform inside and outside services and the Government's response to the Independent inquiry into the death of David Bennett*. London: The Stationery Office.

45. Das Nair, R. & Butler, C. (Eds.). (2012). *Intersectionality, sexuality and psychological therapies: Working with lesbian, gay and bisexual diversity*. Chichester: Wiley.

46. Caplan, P.J. & Cosgrove, L. (Eds.) (2004). *Bias in psychiatric diagnosis.* New York: Rowman & Littlefield.

47. Metzl, J. (2009).) *The protest psychosis: How schizophrenia became a black disease.* Boston, MA: Beacon Press.

48. Chadwick, P.K. (1997). *Schizophrenia: The positive perspective.* London: Routledge.

49. Van Putten, T. & May, P.R. (1978). Subjective response as a predictor of outcome in pharmacotherapy. *Archives of General Psychiatry, 35,* 477–480. http://archpsyc.jamanetwork.com/article.aspx?articleid=491900

50. Van Putten, T., May, P.R. & Marder, S.R. (1984). Akathisia with haloperidol and thiothixene. *Archives of General Psychiatry, 41,* 1036–1039. http://archpsyc.jamanetwork.com/article.aspx?articleid=493445

51. Mosher, L.R., Gosden, R. & Beder, S. (2004). Drug companies and schizophrenia: Unbridled capitalism meets madness. In J. Read, L.R. Mosher & R. Bentall, *Models of madness: Psychological, social and biological approaches to schizophrenia* (pp.115–130). New York, NY: Brunnel-Routledge. www.uow.edu.au/~sharonb/drugcompanies.html

52. Magliano, L., Read, J., Sagliocchi, A., Patalano, M., D'Ambrosio, A. & Oliviero, N. (2013) Differences in views of schizophrenia during medical education: A comparative study of 1st vs. 5th-6th year Italian medical students? *Social Psychiatry and Psychiatric Epidemiology, 48,* 1647–1655. http://link.springer.com/article/10.1007%2Fs00127-012-0610-x

53. Pavilion Publishing (2014, January 14). *Psychosis Revisited* (2nd edn.) Retrieved 7 March 2014 from www.pavpub.com/psychosis-revisited-2nd-edition/

54. Health & Care Professions Council (2012). *Standards of education and training: Your duties as an education provider.* London: HCPC. https://www.hcpc-uk.org/assets/ documents/100029 5EStandardsofeducationandtraining-fromSeptember2009.pdf

55. Patel, N., Bennett, E., Dennis, M., Dosanjh, et al. (Eds.) (2000). *Clinical psychology, 'race' & culture: A training manual.* Leicester: BPS Books.

56. Division of Clinical Psychology. (2016). *DCP Inclusivity Strategy 2016-2018.* Leicester: British Psychological Society.

57. Kinderman, P. (2014). *A prescription for psychiatry.* London: Palgrave Macmillan.

58. Onyett, S. (2014, February 14). *What will help prevent tragedies like Mid Staffs happening again? Time for a shift in attention. Discursive of Tunbridge Wells: The Salomons blog: Views and commentary on psychology, mental health and other stuff. Tunbridge Wells, Kent.* Retrieved 21 March 2014 from http://discursiveoftunbridgewells.blogspot.co.uk/search/label/Steve%20Onyett%20%28Author%29

Section 14

1. Laurance, J. (2013, November 17). *A journey to the heart of Africa's Aids epidemic.* Retrieved May 23, 2014, from www.independent.co.uk/news/world/africa/a-journey-to-the-heart-of-africas-aids-epidemic-8945522.html

2. Johnstone, L. & Dallos, R. (2013). *Formulation in psychology and psychotherapy.* Hove: Routledge.

3. Braehler, C., Valiquette, L., Holowka, D., Malla, A.K., Joober, R., Ciampi, A., Pawliuk, N. & King, S. (2013). Childhood trauma and dissociation in first-episode psychosis, chronic schizophrenia and community controls. *Psychiatry Research, 210*(1). www.sciencedirect.com/science/ article/ pii/S0165178113003119

4. Wilkinson, R. & Pickett, K. (2010). *The spirit level: Why equality is better for everyone.* London: Penguin.

5. Jacobs, D. (1994). Environmental failure-oppression is the only cause of psychopathology. *Journal of Mind and Behavior, 15*(1 & 2), 1–18. www.brown.uk.com/brownlibrary/DJH.htm

6. Karlsen, S. & Nazroo, J.Y. (2004). Fear of racism and health. *Journal of Epidemiology and Community Health, 58*(12), 1017-1018. http://jech.bmj.com/content/58/12/1017.full

7. McKenzie, K. (2003). Racism and health: Antiracism is an important health issue. *British Medical Journal, 326*(7380), 65-66. www.ncbi.nlm.nih.gov/pmc/articles/PMC1125019/

8. Nazroo, J.Y. (2003). The structuring of ethnic inequalities in health: Economic position, racial discrimination, and racism. *American Journal of Public Health, 93*(2), 277–284. www.ncbi.nlm.nih.gov/pmc/articles/PMC1447729/

9. Frenk, J. (2014, December 17). *Racism and public health: Statement from Dean Julio Frenk.* Retrieved 21 December 2016 from www.hsph.harvard.edu/news/features/racism-and-public-health-statement-from-dean-julio-frenk/

10. New Economics Foundation (2008). *New Economics Foundation.* Retrieved 12 November 2013 from www.neweconomicsfoundation.org

11. Division of Clinical Psychology (2000). *Recent advances in understanding mental illness and psychotic experiences*, p.71. Leicester: British Psychological Society.

12. Wikipedia (2013, December 05). *News values.* Retrieved 21 March 2014 from http:// en.wikipedia.org/wiki/News_values

13. Perkins, R. (2000). *I have a vision ... Beyond deficit and discrimination. Overcoming the barriers and meeting the challenges of the 21st century.* Millennium mental health conference. Nottingham: BRIJ Consultancy.

Lightning Source UK Ltd.
Milton Keynes UK
UKHW052232211222
414259UK00005B/15